Technology Activities

Jenny Davies

Bright Ideas
for Early Years

Published by Scholastic Publications Ltd,
Villiers House, Clarendon Avenue,
Leamington Spa, Warwickshire,
CV32 5PR

© 1992 Scholastic Publications Ltd
    Reprinted 1993

Written by Jenny Davies
Edited by Christine Lee
Sub-edited by Robin Hunt and Catherine
Baker
Illustrations by David McTaggart

Cover photograph by Martyn Chillmaid

Photographs by Chris Kelly (pages 9 and
71), Isabelle Butchinsky (page 21), Bob
Bray (pages 31 and 49), R J Davis (page
39), John Twinning (page 65) and Janet
Harber (page 81)

The publishers wish to thank Danny
Nuttall and Lettie and Mallory Hogston
for their help in the preparation of the
front cover of this book.

Artwork by
Liz Preece, Castle Graphics, Kenilworth,

Printed in Great Britain by Loxley
Brothers Ltd, Sheffield

British Library Cataloguing in Publication Data
A catalogue record for this book is available from the British
Library
ISBN 0590 53007-0

Contents

Introduction

Within the early years curriculum, technology is a relatively
new area, and as such has left many people wondering, 'What
is technology?', 'Why do children need technological
capability?' and 'What is the framework in which we should
work?' These three questions are considered in more detail
overleaf.

What do we mean by 'technology'?

Many attempts have been made to define technology. The Concise Oxford Dictionary defines it as 'the (science of) practical or industrial art(s), ethnological study of development of such arts; application of science'. Perhaps we could think of technology more easily as the systematic use of materials and ideas which satisfy a human need to enhance or influence our life style.

Stone Age man became 'technological man' with the use of the first tool and the deliberate use of fire to keep wild animals at bay. Similarly, the use of Stone Age implements to make cave markings and pictures was satisfying the basic human need for self-expression and communication.

Today, examples of technological advance abound. All around us are the products of technology:
• artefacts (objects which have been made by people);
• systems (sets of objects or activities which together perform a specific task);
• environments (surroundings which have been deliberately made or developed by people).

Our motorway network or our postal delivery service are both examples of sophisticated systems put into place to satisfy human need. A simple shop, as well as being an environment, must furthermore operate a well-defined system in order to offer its service. The making of a cup of tea or coffee is a system in that it also follows a well-defined set of operations. A computer is more complex than an artefact in that it contains electrical systems. A hand-operated egg whisk is also a system, however, in that it is made up of movable parts which work together in a systematic manner.

Artefacts, such as cups, saucers, milk

bottles, hammers, nails, sculptures, typewriters, tables and countless other objects, are all examples of technology. Each has been made for a specific purpose, in a specific manner, using the appropriate materials.

Why do children need technological capability?

Children are growing up in a complex world and as educators we must help them to understand, to evaluate and then to contribute to the world in which they live.

In order to understand the world, young children must begin by exploring their immediate environment and neighbourhood. This can be done in several ways, one of the best being to take them out on visits. The visits need not be difficult to arrange. A walk down the street looking at buildings or a walk to the shops or to post a letter could be the starting point for a topic which would include technology work. Role-play is another important means through which children learn about and come to terms with the world around them. A visit to a hairdresser's shop or a hairdresser coming to visit the children and talking about their work could be made more valuable by setting up a role-play hairdresser's shop (using real, but safe, equipment). Other role-play areas could include shops of various kinds: a café, a travel agent, a post office, a garage or a room of a house such as a lounge.

Increasingly, adults must be able to evaluate the effect of technology on the environment and adapt accordingly if we are to avoid ruining our planet. Children must be taught to address this question and even the very youngest children can be encouraged to look around them and conduct litter searches or evaluate how well the school grounds are used for recreation and conservation.

If children are taught to understand and care for the world around them and are also taught various technological skills, such as problem-solving, together with the appropriate use of materials, they will develop an important life skill.

Problem-solving is ubiquitous in adult life and so this training will prove invaluable to them, both personally and professionally.

What framework should we use?

Technology is such a wide and complex area that to contain even the basics of it within a school curriculum is a daunting prospect. Another difficulty, when working in this sphere, is how to decide whether an activity is 'technology'.

The following checklist, adapted from the Technology National Curriculum document (1990), may form a useful framework in which to plan work and to answer the question, 'Is it technology?'
● Does the activity cover at least one of the attainment targets?
● Are the children helping to make or finding out about artefacts, systems or environments?
● Are the children working on a topic which contains any of the following strands: developing and using systems; working with materials; developing and communicating ideas; satisfying human need?
● Are the topics cross-curricular and do they contain elements of art and design, business studies, CDT, home economics or IT?

Obviously any one activity or topic could not contain all of these elements. Common sense must apply in planning technology so that the activity contains a balance of the elements required.

Many of the activities found in the following chapters may be familiar but may not have been thought of as technology before. Familiar activities can often be taken a step further, perhaps by evaluating the outcome through discussion afterwards, or by asking the children to suggest ideas about how things might be done.

It should be remembered that in early years teaching, there must be a 'pre-technology' stage just as there are pre-number, pre-reading and pre-writing stages. The children may be concentrating on the most basic skills of using adhesives, paint and scissors, of seeing shapes and sizes in the objects around them or of playing in the home corner.

Good early years teaching will inevitably include technology, but by consciously structuring activities and topics with technology in mind, you will give the children the opportunity to develop technological capability as a life skill.

Nursery rhymes and songs

Chapter one

Nursery rhymes and songs are an inevitable and important part of young children's experience. They offer an ideal starting point for active learning and are a rich source of opportunities for developing concepts and skills in technology.

In this chapter, traditional problem-solving approaches are used to encourage children to think out for themselves how various tasks might be performed. The activities are naturally stimulated by familiar nursery rhymes or songs, and during each task, the children produce systems or artefacts. There is also the opportunity to produce a plan of an environment (children's playground) in one of the activities.

Opportunities for role-play, which is a vital part of early years learning experiences, are suggested, as are visits. Visits are often difficult to arrange, but well worth the effort, as they make the activity so much more relevant to the child. Through these activities, children will gain experience in the context of home ('Incy Wincy Spider'), shops ('Polly put the kettle on'), work ('London Bridge'), hospital or doctor's ('Humpty Dumpty'), recreation ('See-saw, Margery Daw') and transport ('The wheels on the bus' and 'The Owl and the Pussy-cat').

All the activities provide ample opportunity for the extension of language and art work.

Incy Wincy Spider

Incy Wincy Spider
Climbed the water spout,
Down came the rain
And washed poor Incy out.
Out came the sun
And dried up all the rain,
So Incy Wincy Spider
Climbed the spout again.
Traditional

Hanging by a thread

Objective

To examine the relative strengths of different types of thread.

What you need

Various threads (such as cotton, wool, string), adhesive tape, paper, pencil, scissors, Plasticine, copies of photocopiable page 91.

What to do

This activity is best undertaken on a bright autumn morning when it will be easy to find spiders' webs.

Before the activity, draw two outlines of a spider on to paper, then cut them out. Stick the two shapes together, placing a lump of Plasticine between them to add weight.

Say the rhyme 'Incy Wincy Spider' with the children, then take them on a walk around the school grounds looking for spiders' webs. (Make sure you are already aware of where webs are likely to be found. Hedges are ideal for this.) Get them to observe closely the shapes of the webs, and the thread.

Back in the classroom, tell the children that they are going to make a web for the model spider, but they must make sure that the thread is strong enough to support the spider.

Show the children the various threads and discuss ways of testing their strength using the model spider. Following their suggestions wherever possible, stick or tie each thread to the spider and suspend it for a few seconds. (Make sure that at least one thread will snap.)

What you need

A saucer of water, a damp tea-towel, a bowl of water.

What to do

Talk with the children about how the sun dries up rain puddles. Ask them to think of something else that is put outside to dry. Ask them what weather is best for drying the washing. Let the children put a saucer of water outside and observe how long it takes to dry up. Make sure they note the current weather.

Give the children a tea-towel or some other small item to wash. Let them hang it out of the window and see how long it takes to dry. Make sure they note the weather. Get them to repeat this activity on another day when the weather is different.

Discussion

Have you ever helped to peg out the washing? What is the best weather for drying the washing? How is the washing dried on a damp or rainy day?

If more than one thread is strong enough, let the children choose which they think will look the nicest on the display. Help the children to make a web from their chosen thread, then staple the spider's web and spider to the wall.

Give each child a copy of photocopiable page 91 on which to record the results of the experiment.

Discussion

We found some thread strong enough for the model spider. What else needs very strong thread? (Encourage answers such as parcels tied with string, ropes for PE, guy ropes on tents.)

Drying outside

Objective

To help the children to understand why washing is often hung outside to dry and how the weather can affect the process.

Humpty Dumpty

Humpty Dumpty sat on a wall,
Humpty Dumpty had a great fall.
All the king's horses and all the king's
     men,
Couldn't put Humpty together again.
Traditional

Putting Humpty back together

Objective

To find out which materials are good for sticking cardboard together and to develop concepts about caring at home.

What you need

Several fairly large cardboard cut-outs of Humpty Dumpty cut into four or five pieces, jam, flour and water for paste, school adhesive, Blu-Tack, adhesive tape, copies of photocopiable page 92.

What to do

Sing 'Humpty Dumpty' with the children. Make a number of cardboard cut-outs of Humpty Dumpty, using Figure 1 for reference. Ask the children to think how they could put Humpty back together again. (Be prepared to incorporate additional sensible suggestions into your plan!)

Show the children the various sticking agents and explain that in groups they are going to try to stick Humpty together again. Give each group the pieces of a cardboard cut-out, a sticking agent (different for each group) and a copy of photocopiable page 92. Ask them to predict which sticking agent will be best before trying to stick the cut-out together.

Hang the cut-out Humpty Dumpties on the wall and, later in the day, look carefully to see which cut-outs have remained stuck together.

The children should record the results on photocopiable page 92 by colouring in the items which best held the cardboard together.

Figure 1

Follow-up

Ask the children to recall who tried to help Humpty Dumpty. Discuss who helps the children when they fall over.

Set up a role-play hospital and allow them to enact a hospital or doctor scene in the role-play area, or to make up their own role-play.

Discussion

Have you ever been hurt at home or at school? Who helped you? Have you ever been to hospital? If so, who was especially kind there?

> ## Polly put the kettle on
>
> Polly put the kettle on,
> Polly put the kettle on,
> Polly put the kettle on,
> We'll all have tea.
> *Traditional*

Tea-time

Objective

To find out how a cup of tea is made.

What you need

Various types of tea-bags, a kettle, a teapot (preferably one which is light coloured inside), cups and saucers, milk, teaspoon.

What to do

Before the activity, check with parents to make sure they have no objections to their children drinking tea.

Sing 'Polly put the kettle on' with the children. Ask the children why they think

Polly didn't make the tea. Where might the people have gone?

Explain to the children that they are going to learn how to make a cup of tea.

Examine different types of tea-bags with the children, noting similarities and differences in shape, texture and perforations. Let the children look inside a tea-bag.

Boil a kettle of water after discussion about the dangers of electricity. Make sure the children keep away from the steam.

Ask them to watch out for the colour change as you pour water into the teapot, and again later when the tea is added to the milk. Let them taste the tea when it is weak and when it is stronger.

Repeat the activity using different tea-bags. Ask the children if they notice any differences in appearance or taste.

Discussion

Did you enjoy making the tea? Why should we keep away from the kettle when it boils? Which tea was the best?

A tea party

Objective
To plan a tea party.

What you need
Tea-bags, a kettle, a teapot, milk, sugar, lemon, biscuits, orange juice, computer and word-processing program (optional).

What to do
Before the activity, make sure parents have no objections to their children drinking tea. Suggest to the children that they might make a tea-party for 'Polly'.

Invite several adults (parents, grandparents, helpers) to an afternoon tea party. Help a group of children to design and make invitations. (The invitations could be word processed if preferred, then the children could add their own designs.)

Discuss with the children what will be needed, then take a small group shopping for the tea party. If possible, let children look at several shops then decide which one they need. Ask other children to set out the cups and saucers, pour the milk or lemon (but not the hot tea) and serve biscuits to the visitors.

Let the children join in the tea party and then share their games and activities with the visitors. Let the children help with the washing-up.

Follow-up
Ask the children to draw what they did to help with the tea party, then sequence the pictures and make them into a book.

Discussion
What was your favourite part of the tea party? How did you help? Did the visitors enjoy themselves? What sort of tea-bags do you use at home?

London Bridge is falling down
London Bridge is falling down,
Falling down, falling down,
London Bridge is falling down,
My fair lady.

Traditional

Building materials

Objective
To find out about building materials.

What you need
Pictures of bridges, access to a building site, bricks and a bucket of mortar from the site, trowel, construction toys such as Mobilo and DUPLO, pencils, paper.

What to do
Sing and play the game 'London Bridge' with the children.

Show the children some pictures of bridges, and ask them to describe them and their usage. Discuss what the bridges might be made from and whether the building materials described in the rhyme are ever used.

Ask the children to make bridges from construction toys such as DUPLO and Mobilo. Test the bridges with a weight. Ask the children to make an observational drawing of their own bridge.

Organise a visit to a building site and ask some of the workmen to tell the children what they are building. Take back a few bricks and a bucket of mortar (again, previously arranged). Let the children help to build a small wall in a corner of the school grounds. This could then be used as a paint pot stand or screen.

Discussion

Why do builders of bridges or buildings not usually use gold or silver? Have you ever seen a picture of a building that does have gold on it? What were the builders we saw using? Is our wall quite strong? Why are the bricks sticking together? Would our school glue have been strong enough?

Let's get moving

Objective

To explore movement by pushing and by using rollers.

What you need

A ramp, items to roll or slide down a ramp (eg, bricks, cylinders, marbles), a toy bus, two broom handles or thick bamboo canes (to be used as rollers), large sturdy cardboard box, toy steering-wheel and peaked cap, paint, adhesive, coloured paper, two small toy buses, a few Play People, a road play mat.

What to do

Let the children roll or slide the items down the ramp. Get them to make a set of objects which roll and a set which slide. Discuss why some might slide and others might roll.

Ask the children to look underneath a toy bus. Get them to predict whether it will roll or slide. Talk about the wheels and how they help the bus to move.

Sing the song 'The wheels on the bus go round and round' with the children.

Show children the large cardboard box and explain that they are going to turn it into a 'bus'. Let them paint it and

15

stick on features such as wheels and windows made from paper.

Ask a child to sit in the bus, holding the steering wheel and wearing the cap. Discuss what might make a real bus move. Ask the children to think of a way to move the pretend bus (by pushing). Show them the two rollers and ask the children to suggest ways of using them to make the bus move more easily. Try out any suggestions the children might make. Hopefully this will include placing the rollers underneath the bus.

Using a play mat, two toy buses and a few Play People, ask the children to work out two bus routes so that the Play People can all be picked up from their bus stops.

Discussion

Why did some things slide down the ramp? Why did some roll? In what ways are the bus rollers a bit like wheels? Why don't the wheels on a real bus keep being left on the floor like our rollers?

The Owl and the Pussy-cat

The Owl and the Pussy-cat went to sea
    In a beautiful pea-green boat,
They took some honey, and plenty of money,
    Wrapped up in a five-pound note.
The Owl looked up to the stars above,
    And sang to a small guitar,
'O lovely Pussy! O Pussy, my love,
    What a beautiful Pussy you are,
        You are,
        You are!
What a beautiful Pussy you are!'

Edward Lear

Floating and sinking

Objective

To find out about floating and sinking.

What you need

A variety of objects for floating and sinking, a water tray, Play People, polystyrene trays, cartons, lids, straws, paper, inner tubes from toilet rolls, adhesive tape, paper-clips, Blu-Tack, scissors, a computer with a word processing program (optional).

What to do

Allow free play with the water tray using objects for floating and sinking.

Ask the children to collect together a set of objects which float and a set which sink.

Sing or say 'The Owl and the Pussy-cat' with the children.

Suggest to the children that they are going to make a boat for a Play Person. Show them the collection of trays, cartons, lids, straws, paper and toilet roll tubes.

Ask the children to choose something to use as the base of the boat and to test it to see whether it floats. Then let the children choose other items to add as sails, cabins etc, finding the best way of securing them to the base.

Let them test the boat again. If it tips over, ask the children to consider why this might happen and what might be taken off, and to test it again. When the boat floats, let the children test it with a Play Person. Ask them to try to find a way to move the boat along the water, such as by pushing, flicking the water or blowing.

Follow-up

Let the children make a concertina book to show how the boat was made, with captions and pictures on each page. The sequence should illustrate the separate parts used, the child making the boat, and the boat sailing. The front of the book could show the Owl and the Pussy-cat in their boat. A word processor could be used for the captions, if preferred.

Discussion

Were you pleased with your boat? Was it difficult to make it so that it didn't tip up? If it tipped up at first, how did you change it? Would the Owl and the Pussy-cat have liked your boat? How would a real boat have moved?

> ## Rock-a-bye baby
> Rock-a-bye baby,
> On the tree top,
> When the wind blows,
> The cradle will rock;
> When the bough breaks
> The cradle will fall,
> Down will come baby,
> Cradle and all.
> *Traditional*

Blowing in the wind

Objective
To investigate the effects of the wind on various materials.

What you need
Strips of tissue paper, twigs, container tall enough to support the twigs (such as a large yoghurt or cream pot), Plasticine, tin foil, paper, adhesive tape, a baby Play Person, a hair drier.

What to do
Take the children outside on a windy day and ask them to look for any visible effects of the wind on trees, washing or smoke. Ask some of the children to run, holding strips of tissue paper, while others watch what happens to the paper. Discuss why the paper might be moving.

Sing the nursery rhyme 'Rock-a-bye Baby' with the children, then tell them that they are going to make a cradle which will not fall when the wind blows.

Show the children the twigs and explain that these will represent the trees, then show them the materials they can use to make a cradle. Explain that the Plasticine and the tin foil can be moulded but adhesive tape will be needed if paper is chosen.

Place the twigs in the container, then ask the children to test each cradle by balancing it loosely on the twigs, then blowing the cradle gently with a hair drier. Tell them to watch whether the twigs bend and the cradles fall.

When a suitable cradle has been found, ask the children to place a Play Person baby in it and test again.

Follow-up
Let the children use samples of the materials tested for the cradles and drop them from a height. Get them to watch carefully how they fall. The activity could be repeated, positioning the hair drier so that items drop through the current of air.

Discussion
Why did the tissue paper move when we ran? Did the twigs move when we blew the hair drier? Which materials fell out of the 'tree' when we blew the hair drier? What happened when we dropped them from a height? Which materials blew away when we dropped them using the hair drier? Why do you think the Plasticine didn't blow away?

See-saw for teddy

Objective
To investigate the relative strengths of different materials.

What you need
Strips of paper, cardboard and balsa-wood of equal lengths, a ruler, a wooden brick, weights, two small teddies.

What to do
Sing the rhyme with the children. Discuss see-saws and what might have happened to Margery Daw if the see-saw had bent or broken.

Tell the children that they are going to make a see-saw strong enough to be used by two teddies. Ask the children to predict whether the paper, cardboard, balsa-wood or ruler will make the strongest see-saw.

Ask the children to test in turn the strips of paper, cardboard and balsa-wood, and the ruler as a see-saw, using the wooden brick as a fulcrum. Let them put a weight on one end and try to press the other end down using their fingers. Ask the children to use the strongest material to make a see-saw for the two teddies.

Let the children play with the see-saw — one child holding the see-saw on the brick and another holding the teddies on and pushing them up and down.

Discussion
We had to hold our model see-saw on the brick so that it didn't fall off. On a real see-saw, how is it fastened on? Could we have fastened our see-saw to the brick? What could we have used to hold it in place?

Swings and slides

Objective
To consider safety in the playground and to reinforce the concept of distance.

What you need
Copies of photocopiable page 93, coloured paper, adhesive.

What to do
Discuss where see-saws are usually found and whether Margery Daw might have been playing in a children's playground. Give the children copies of page 93 and let them cut the items out and arrange them on the coloured paper.

When the children are satisfied with their design arrangements, let them stick the items in place. It may be necessary to discuss, for example, why the items should be well spaced out and why flowers might be better round the edge rather than in the middle.

Discussion
On your playground design, did you put the swings too near anything? What might have happened?

Story-time

Chapter two

Young children love stories and, through listening to them (and eventually reading them for themselves), are able to extend their knowledge and understanding of the world. Story characters and situations become very real to children and are, therefore, ideal starting points for developing language and learning skills.

Stories can provide a particularly fertile ground for exploring aspects of technology, and in this chapter ideas are suggested for activities based on some popular stories, both traditional and modern. In each case it is assumed that the teacher will read or tell the story to the children first, providing a real context for the activity.

The first five activities in this chapter explore traditional technological activities as the children find out about and use their knowledge of strength of materials, waterproofing and methods of sticking and fastening. They are also asked to 'design and make', either individually or in groups.

In the rest of the chapter technology takes place in a wide context, for instance, in thinking about shops, or how materials and clothes are suited for their purpose.

The Three Little Pigs

Objective

To test the relative strengths of different materials.

What you need

A copy of *The Three Little Pigs*, illustrated by Stephen Cartwright (Usborne First Stories), straw, twigs, large wooden construction bricks, hair drier, two chairs, a weight, adhesive tape, string, paper.

What to do

Read the story of the Three Little Pigs. Ask the children to work in groups of three or four to try to make a house which will not blow down with the hair drier. Each group should use either straw, twigs or bricks. Let them use string or adhesive tape to help them if necessary. Paper can be used to make a roof.

Test the strength of the houses using the hair drier. Results may vary, so be prepared to discuss factors such as weight, shape of bricks, lightness of straw and whether the string or adhesive tape has been useful.

Carry out a second test by placing some straw across two chairs, then testing its strength with a weight. Repeat the experiment using some twigs and a brick. The materials could also be tested by a child stepping on the material between the chairs. Lift the child on, but be ready to catch him! Help from another adult might be advisable.

Discussion

Which house do you think the three pigs would like to have lived in? Why? Which material was the strongest? How could you tell? When we put a weight on the material, what exactly happened? Did it bend, break or stay firm? Which building material was the weakest?

The Little Red Hen

Objectives
To design and make a strong bag.

What you need
A copy of *The Little Red Hen* by Margot Zemach (Hutchinson), various types of paper including tissue paper and brown wrapping paper, scissors, cotton thread, wool, string, adhesive tape, weights, elastic, felt-tipped pens.

What to do
Read the story of the Little Red Hen, then ask each child to make masks of each of the animals in the story. Help them to cut out the masks and attach a piece of elastic.

Ask each child to choose a piece of paper and attempt to make a bag (without handles), using adhesive tape for fastening.

Help the children to test each bag by putting a weight inside it. Discuss which were the best designs, ie those which stuck together on three sides and those which had strong paper. Using the results of this experiment, let the children have another attempt at making a strong bag. Allow them to make handles for their bags, using cotton thread, wool or string. Discuss how the children have positioned the handles and test the bags again.

Act out the story of the Little Red Hen together several times. Let the children use masks and the bags as props. Allow the children to explore the story on their own in full role-play.

Follow-up
Make a collection of commercially produced bags (paper, plastic, biodegradable). Let the children identify which shops they are from and discuss what they are used for.

Discussion
Why did the Little Red Hen's bag need to be strong? Which paper and handles were the best? Why? What happens to all the old bags we throw away? What would happen if we buried them for a long time?

Silly Charlie

Objective
To find material suitable for making a boat.

What you need
A copy of *Silly Charlie* by Joan Hickson (Methuen; out of print – try libraries), various types of paper including tissue paper and greaseproof paper, silver foil, polythene, scissors, adhesive tape, paper-clips, LEGO figures, water tray, cassette recorder.

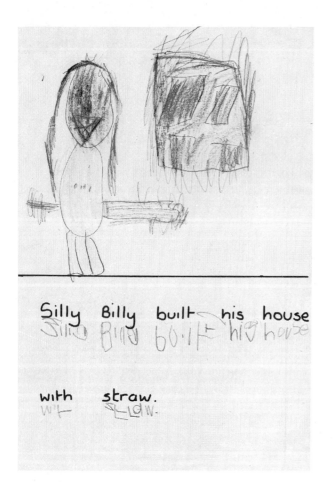

What to do
Read *Silly Charlie* with the children. Discuss how Silly Charlie used the wrong material to make his boat. Ask the children to help Silly Charlie to make a boat that will not fall to pieces in the water.

Cut the paper, foil and polythene into squares. Let each child choose a square and put it in the water. Leave these for a few hours, then later in the day get the children to look at what has happened. Ask them to collect together a set of materials which disintegrate in water and a set which remains firm.

Allow the children to mould or tape new squares of the suitable material into boat shapes. Paper-clips may be useful for fastening. Test the boats for floating capability.

When the children are satisfied with their boats, let them put the LEGO figures into them to represent Silly Charlie. Let the children float their boats on the water tray.

Follow-up
Ask the children to make up similar stories about someone who is silly and makes something out of the wrong material before putting it right. Let them draw two or three pictures to tell their story. Captions could be added, with an adult acting as scribe if necessary.

Ask the children to read the captions or tell the story in their own words and tape record it. Play back the recording to the class, holding up the appropriate pictures.

Discussion
Which paper fell to pieces in the water? Did you make a good boat for Charlie? What was it made of? Did it float when Charlie got in it? Did you like listening to your story on a tape recorder? Did you like the other children's stories?

Winnie the Pooh

Objective
To assess the waterproof properties of different materials.

What you need
A copy of *Piglet is Entirely Surrounded by Water* by A. A. Milne (Little Mammoth), a teddy bear for each child, pieces of fabric including cotton, wool and waterproofed material, polythene, adhesive tape, scissors, string, wool, safety pins, syringes or pipettes.

What to do
Ask each child to bring a teddy bear to school. (Make sure you have a few spare ones for any child who does not have one).

Read the children the story of *Piglet is Entirely Surrounded by Water*.

Discuss rainproof clothes. Ask the children to choose a piece of material and place it on the table in front of them. Let the children drip water on to their pieces of material using the syringes or pipettes. After a few seconds get the children to feel the table under the material to find out whether the water has seeped through. Discard any material which has let water through.

Ask the children to choose some waterproof material with which to make hats and capes for the teddy bears.

Allow the children time to try various ways of making hats and capes and to use their own ideas for attaching string or wool for tying the articles. Encourage them to make sure the capes and hats fit the appropriate teddies. Let the children make observational drawings of their teddies in their capes and hats.

Get the children to test capes and hats by dripping water on them and feeling whether the teddy has remained dry underneath.

Conclude the activity by asking the children to retell the story, using teddies as characters.

Discussion
How do you stay dry on a wet day? Are your rainy-day clothes made of special material? What happens to the rain on an umbrella or a raincoat?

Sleeping Beauty

Objective

To observe how construction toys and boxes can be fastened together.

What you need

Construction toys, junk boxes, large cardboard boxes, adhesive, adhesive tape, string, paper-clips, paper.

What to do

Tell the children that they are going to make a tall tower for the singing game 'There was a princess long ago'.

Ask individuals or pairs of children to make tall towers from construction toys such as Poleidoblocs, or similar wooden bricks, or DUPLO bricks. Ask them to take turns to tell the rest of the class how their tower fastens together.

Ask the children to make some more towers from junk boxes. Help them to test for stability before they fasten or stick the boxes together. Let the children choose how they are going to stick their boxes together. They could, for example, use adhesive, adhesive tape or paper-clips. Encourage the children to devise a fair test to find out which method produces the strongest towers.

As a class make a large tower using large cardboard boxes. Ask the children to decide which way they are going to stick the boxes together, basing their decisions upon their previous experiments. Make sure the children test that the cardboard boxes have stuck together firmly.

Ask the children to suggest ways of representing plants growing around the tower. They could, for example, use string with paper leaves stuck on.

Sing together and dramatise the song with the children standing around the tower.

Draw pictures of the activities and the song.

Follow-up

Use the tower for free play.

Discussion

What made our towers firm and strong? How many boxes were in the big class tower? Were there more pieces in your construction toy towers? What things did not stick very well together?

The Shopping Basket

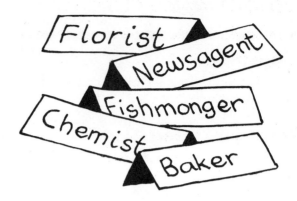

Objective
To find out about different shops.

What you need
Copies of *The Shopping Basket* by John Burningham (Armada Books) and *The Supermarket Mice* by Margaret Gordon (Picture Puffins), card, scissors, felt-tipped pen, real objects which could be bought from different sorts of shops, toy money, copies of photocopiable page 94, table(s).

What to do
Before the activity, prepare some cards with different shop names on them, such as baker, newsagent, greengrocer,

grocer and chemist. Read together *The Shopping Basket* and *The Supermarket Mice*, then discuss going shopping.

Choose several children to be shopkeepers and give each one a card with their shop name. Place the box of objects in the middle of the room, then let the children take turns to choose one and try to place it in front of the right shopkeeper (be prepared to recap on the discussion and read out the name of each shopkeeper's shop).

Place one or two objects from each shop on a table as a reminder. Get the children to fill in the photocopiable page 94 by choosing which shop the picture will become and drawing appropriate objects in the window.

Follow-up
Use the real objects for free play. Use separate tables or boxes for the different shops or divide a long table using wool or string.

Let the children play 'Shopping Lotto' (E. J. Arnold).

Discussion
Do you ever go shopping? Who do you go with? Are the shops nearby or far away? Which shops do you like best? Do you go to some shops nearly every day? Do you go to other shops only sometimes? Why do you think that is?

Cinderella

Objective
To show that different clothes are suitable for different occasions.

What you need
A collection of plain fabrics, a collection of material which children would consider beautiful (for example, brightly coloured fabric), children's clothes for special occasions, dressing-up clothes.

What to do
Tell the children the story of Cinderella. Ask the children to describe Cinderella's clothes before she went to the ball. Encourage them to consider whether they were suitable for the work she had to do. Ask them to describe the clothes she wore at the ball and why she looked so different.

Ask the children to sort the collection of materials into two sets – a 'plain' set and a 'beautiful' set. Encourage them to consider the colour, pattern and texture of each set.

Ask the children's parents to allow the children to bring in any special clothes such as bridesmaids' dresses or pageboy suits. Ask the children to compare these with clothes worn every day for school.

Follow-up
Let the children sort clothes from the role-play box or school costume box and act out the story of Cinderella.

Discussion
Would you want to go to a party wearing your oldest, dirtiest clothes? How do you think Cinderella felt when she suddenly had a lovely new dress to wear? Why would it be silly to wear a bridesmaid's dress every day at school?

Jack and the Beanstalk

Objective
To develop construction skills.

What you need
Pictures of castles, large rectangular-shaped pieces of card, circles of gold paper, strips of brightly coloured or gold paper, rectangles of red paper, card circles (covered in gold paper), adhesive, scissors, adhesive tape, crayons, paper, stapler.

What to do
Tell the children the story of Jack and the Beanstalk. Explain to the children that they are going to work in groups to make different parts of the giant's castle.

Ask one group to find out how to make turret shapes from rectangles of card. Gold paper circles can be added to the top of the turrets, either flat or as a cone, depending on what ideas the children have. Ask another group to study carefully the pictures of castles, then draw rampart shapes on card and cut them out. Let a third group cover a teacher's chair with strips of gold or coloured paper to make the giant's chair. Allow liberal use of adhesive tape. Ask a fourth group to stick red rectangles of paper in a brick pattern on to large pieces of card for the castle walls.

Staple the turrets, ramparts and bricks to the walls of the role-play area. Arrange the furniture to make the interior of the giant's castle. Use gold coloured card for the giant's money. Use the castle for free role-play.

Follow-up
Get the children to draw and write about making the castle.

Discussion
Did you think that a flat piece of card could be made into a turret shape? What is that shape called? How do you feel when you are sitting in the castle? Are you frightened by the giant?

Smith the Lonely Hedgehog

Objective
To use role-play to help children understand the world around them.

What you need
A copy of *Smith the Lonely Hedgehog* by Althea (Dinosaur Books; out of print — try libraries), a blanket, Plasticine, art straws, scissors, leaves, brown paint, cardboard.

What to do
This activity is recommended after discussing autumn leaves and hibernation. Read with the children *Smith the Lonely Hedgehog*.

Place a blanket on the floor, with a group of children sitting around it, their legs underneath. Tell them to lie down under the blanket and pretend to hibernate. As they are lying down, describe in as much detail as possible how it will be daytime and night-time many times over, but they must remain asleep, hibernating like hedgehogs.

Describe some of the activities children would be doing while hedgehogs sleep.

Describe also how the cold winter weather will come, maybe it will snow and children will make snowmen, Christmas will come and go but still the hedgehogs stay asleep. The children will love being snuggled together under the blanket, but when you describe the warm spring weather encourage them to pretend to wake up and crawl out of their winter blanket and look for food.

Let the children make a model hedgehog from Plasticine. Ask them to cut up and paint art straws and stick them on as spikes. Place the model on a cardboard base and spread real autumn leaves around it.

Discussion
Did you like pretending to be a hedgehog? Do you think a hedgehog would be hungry when it woke up in the spring? What would have kept it warm all through the cold weather? What keeps you warm in bed?

The Snowman

Objective
To help children understand the concepts of melting and freezing.

What you need
A copy of *The Snowman* by Raymond Briggs (Picture Puffin), snow, access to a fridge or a freezer and a radiator, white tissue paper, strips of fabric, scissors, white wool, adhesive, card.

What to do
This activity should be undertaken on a snowy day.

Look carefully at the pictures in the book of *The Snowman*.

Take the children outside and ask them each to make a miniature snowman on a piece of card.

Recall the places favoured by the Snowman and find similar cold places for some of the children's snowmen, such as in a fridge or a freezer, outside or near a door. Put other snowmen in places not favoured by the Snowman in the story, such as near a fire or radiator or in a hot room. Leave the snowmen for a while and later discuss what has happened.

Let the children whose snowmen have melted make a second snowman and place them in one of the cold places so that they last longer.

Allow the children to make snowman models by scrunching up some white tissue paper and covering it with a smooth piece wrapped round and tied with white wool in a bundle at the top. Ask them to make a smaller shape for the head and to stick the two shapes together. Let them stick on fabric scraps for facial features. Ask the children to find a way of tying on the strips of material for the scarf. Ask them to design and stick on a hat made from tissue paper.

Discussion
Why do you need to wrap up in snowy weather? Why does the Snowman like it to be cold? What was left when our snowmen melted?

Shapes and sizes

Chapter three

Adults are often surprised at how observant children are and how well they remember details of the world around them. This chapter aims to stimulate and promote this natural skill by making children aware of shape, size and design in the artefacts and environments around them. As children become aware of the design make-up of the world around them, they will become more able to contribute their own ideas.

Activities in this chapter vary considerably in complexity, ranging from a short game to the making of a role-play environment (a newsagent's shop), which incorporates the study of shapes and sizes within it.

Several of the activities would be suitable as part of an ongoing topic or project, for example, looking at shapes in houses and making a model house, making a newsagent's shop, and identifying the growth and skills acquired by babies and toddlers. Other activities would be more suitable at specific times, such as 'Which puddle?' on a rainy day.

Looking at houses

Objective
To help children become aware of shapes and patterns in houses.

What you need
Pictures of houses, paper, pencils, clip-boards, various samples of fabrics and paper, clear polythene.

What to do
Show the children pictures of houses and discuss with them the differences in shape and size of windows, roofs and general outline.

Equip the children with paper, pencils and a clip-board, and then take them outside to look at the brick patterns on school walls or nearby houses. Walk to the nearest houses and ask the children to observe closely the shape and size of windows, roofs and general outline. Ask the children to draw the houses. They may like to draw the houses again back in the classroom using their first drawing to help them remember.

Show the children various sorts of paper, fabric and clear polythene. Discuss which would be best to use on a model house for the windows and what shapes the polythene would need to be cut into.

Discussion
Were the windows of the houses all the same? Are the windows in our classroom a different shape from the house windows? Is glass good for windows? What were the roofs like? Were the door patterns circles or rectangles or another shape? Did you like them?

Make a model house

Objective
To make children aware of shape in the construction of a model house.

What you need
Four large cardboard boxes, several different samples of commercially produced wallpaper, a piece of carpet or thick material, a large piece of cardboard, syringes or pipettes, a jug, towel, cardboard tubes, a variety of papers, scissors, clear polythene, white paper, crayons, pencils, felt-tipped pens, candles, adhesive, adhesive tape, cotton reels, sponges, paint.

What to do

Show the children the boxes. Discuss how they could be arranged to make a model house or bungalow with four rooms or a block of four flats. Discuss the differences between these types of homes. Let the children choose which type of home to make, then help them to stick the boxes together.

Look at some samples of commercially produced wallpaper, then ask the children to print their own, using cotton reels, cardboard tubes or sponges. Ask the children to help you measure their wallpaper for the model house by holding it next to the wall and cutting it. Older children may be able to use non-standard measures for themselves. Let the children stick the paper to the inside walls of the model. Measure and cut suitable carpet material in the same way.

Fold a piece of cardboard to form an apex roof shape and drip water on to it carefully using a jug. Ask the children to watch carefully to find out whether the 'rain' runs off the roof or stays on it in puddles. Set up a similar test with a flat piece of card. (Have a towel handy during these tests.) Ask the children to choose which shape they think would be best for the roof. Add the appropriate roof to the model.

Show the children a cardboard tube and ask them to suggest ways of making a gutter shape from it. Help the children with cutting the tubes in the way they suggest. Help them to attach the gutters using adhesive tape.

Cut out holes for windows and ask the children to cut a similar shape out of clear polythene. Let them stick the windows in place using adhesive tape.

Offer the children several paper rectangles to colour using pencils, wax crayons, coloured candles and felt-tipped pens. Let them drip water on to the rectangles using syringes or pipettes. Ask them to rub the paper lightly to find out which are waterproof and therefore suitable for making roof and wall tiles for the house. Ask the children to stick the tiles on to the model house.

Making a newsagent's shop

Objective
To observe pattern and shape while making articles for the role-play shop.

What you need
Liquorice allsorts, different colours of modelling clay, rectangular pieces of wood or thick cardboard, silver foil, paper, crayons, stapler, adhesive, word processor, old greetings cards, toy money.

What to do
Discuss newsagents' shops and what they sell. Let groups of children try out the following activities to make items for their own 'shop':
• Encourage the children to look carefully at the shapes, sizes and patterns of liquorice allsorts. Allow them to take some of them to pieces.

Give the children some pieces of modelling clay in different colours and ask them to make models of the liquorice allsorts.

Give the children each a small rectangular piece of wood or thick cardboard and a piece of silver foil. Ask them to make model chocolate bars by covering the rectangle with foil without wasting any of it. Let them design a wrapper and stick it in place around the foil. Choose a few chocolate bar models and ask the children to copy them so that the shop can sell sets of the same type of bar.
• Show the children a collection of old greetings cards. Give each child a card and ask them to fold a piece of paper in half to make a simple envelope. Discuss the size of the envelope and make adjustments before sticking the sides with adhesive.

• After the children have written their own 'news' for the week, ask a parent or helper to type each child's news into the computer and make several print-outs. Children can help to take a page from each set of print-outs and fold or staple these together to make newspapers for the shop. (A4 size print-outs could be stuck on to larger paper to make realistic newspaper sizes).

Use the shop for free role-play. Ask older children to come to 'buy' the various items with toy money.

Discussion
Did your model sweets look similar to the real sweets? Were the layers on your sweets the same size as each other? Would they have been the same size if you had put layers of rolled out dough on top of each other, and then done the cutting out? Did your envelopes fit the greetings cards? Did you like having your news in our own newspapers?

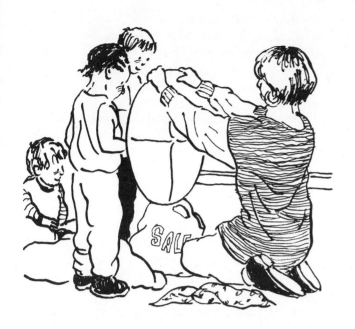

Repeat this with rectangular, square and triangular shaped material.

Follow-up
Ask the children how many children they think could sit on, stand on and stand round the various shaped pieces of material. Count how many actually can.

Discussion
Could more children sit on the mats or stand on them? Could more or less children than you thought sit on the mat?

Which puddle?

Objective
To estimate the size and shape of a puddle.

What you need
Six pieces of sugar paper (two pieces should be quite large), a cup of water, several towels.

What to do
Show the children three different-sized pieces of sugar paper. Discuss rainy days and tell the children you are going to pretend it is raining in the classroom. Ask the children which size of paper they think will be completely covered with water if a cup full of water is dripped on to it. Surround the paper with towels and test by carefully pouring a cup of water on to each piece of paper. Discuss which paper was covered by the water and whether any of them were too small so that the water spilled over the sides. Look carefully to see whether any of the pieces of paper were much bigger than the 'puddle'.

Repeat the activity with half a cup of water using new pieces of sugar paper.

What is it like?

Objective
To think about shape and estimate sizes.

What you need
A circular piece of fabric about one metre in diameter and edged in a different colour, similar sized pieces of fabric in square, rectangle and triangle shapes.

What to do
Fold the circular material into sixteen segments. Show the children the folded shape and ask them what it reminds them of. They might suggest a folded umbrella or a long thin leaf. Unfold the material so that the shape is now an eighth of a circle and ask the children to think of some more items (a piece of pie, an ice-cream cone). Repeat this with a quarter circle showing, then a semicircle, then a full circle.

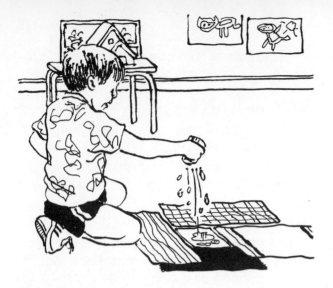

Follow-up

Pour a small amount of water on to a piece of absorbent paper and quickly draw an outline around the water. Let the children watch the water being soaked up by the paper. Draw a second outline around the damp paper. Compare the two outlines.

Discussion

Did you think the first puddle would be larger or smaller than it was? Did you guess the right size? Have you ever splashed through rain puddles outside on a wet day? Why do we have grids along the roadside? Do you know where the rain goes to?

Shape books

Objective

To help children notice shapes and sizes in the world around them.

What you need

Coloured paper cut into circles, squares, rectangles and triangles, coloured pencils.

What to do

Take the children on a 'shape walk' around the school, having asked them to look for a particular shape, such as circles or squares. (Make sure that you know where at least a few of the shapes can be found beforehand, although children will probably find many more.)

Using Figure 1 for reference, make a number of pages of shapes for each child. The first page should be a simple pattern of, for instance, triangles. The second page should be a shape picture, where children colour only the triangles. The third page should be for the children to draw their own pictures, incorporating at least one triangle. Repeat this format with other shapes.

Cut out different sized triangles, circles, squares and rectangles out of coloured paper and let children make up their own pictures. Suggest to the children that they try different arrangements to make pictures before they decide which they will stick down.

Discussion

Where was the largest circle you found in school? What was it? Was it part of something else? Can you remember seeing a very small square? What was it? Which shapes were easiest to find? Which were harder?

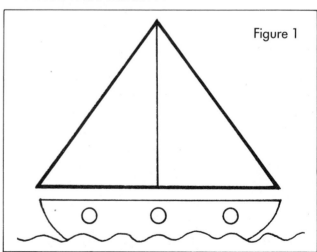

Figure 1

From babies to now

Objective
To consider the development of size and skills from babyhood to early childhood.

What you need
A visit from parents with a new baby, an older baby and a toddler, baby bath and items for bathing a baby, computer with concept keyboard (optional), magazine pictures (optional).

What to do
Use three separate sessions for this activity, if possible.

Arrange to have a new baby brought to the classroom, then a baby who is about six months old, then a toddler.

If possible, ask the parent of the new baby to bath him for the children. Place the bath, with plenty of clean towels around, on the floor so that everyone can see easily. Talk about how the baby is cared for and let each child help to do something for the baby such as taking off a sock, holding the cream, gently washing an arm and so on.

When the older baby visits, discuss what she can do and how much bigger she is than the new-born baby. Look at the size of the clothes.

Repeat this format for the toddler's visit, making comparisons of size and skills.

Make an overlay for a concept keyboard showing the words which will appear on the screen such as 'babies drink milk' or 'babies cannot walk'. Alternatively the overlay could have appropriate pictures from magazines stuck on, so that when the children press a picture, the appropriate phrase appears on the screen.

Let the children take turns at using the concept keyboard to write about the visits. Make a print-out on which the children can draw or stick appropriate pictures.

Discussion
Did you like the babies' clothes? How were they different from your clothes? What can you do that the babies could not do?

Making a pet shop

Objectives
To plan what will be needed for a role-play pet shop and to suggest how to make model homes for the pets.

What you need
Paper, felt-tipped pen, pet food, posters, leaflets, pets' toys, soft toys, different sized boxes, adhesive tape, straws, scissors, strips of card, Blu-Tack, fish tanks.

What to do
Ask the children to make a list of what items are to be found in a pet shop. Ask them to help you make a second list of

what they would like in their role-play pet shop. They could include boxes or tins of pet food, posters or leaflets about pet care, pets' toys, hutches or cages and pets.

If there are pets in school such as a rabbit, guinea pig, mouse or hamster, ask the children to look carefully at what their homes are like. Alternatively, ask the children to describe their own pets or show the children some pictures. Discuss how the homes are planned to give shelter, light and shade, warmth and enough room for movement. Ask the children what materials the different pet homes are made from. Compare two different homes such as a fairly large rabbit hutch and a metal cage for a mouse or hamster.

Show the children two different sized boxes and ask them which one would be suitable for a rabbit or guinea pig and which would be suitable for a mouse or hamster in the role-play shop.

Ask the children to suggest how the boxes could be made into the two

homes. Follow the children's suggestions for making some sort of window shape with bars across (they may suggest straws or strips of card for the bars) and a door shape with some sort of fastener (be prepared to start again with another box if the children tell you to cut more than three sides for the door). If the children's idea for a fastener does not work at first, be prepared for another try. Straws, strips of card, adhesive tape and Blu-Tack should eventually give a workable model.

Encourage the children to look carefully at the shapes and sizes which have been used and created in the two prototype models.

When the children are satisfied with the models, tell them that they can now help to make homes for the shop in the same way using much larger boxes which can also be painted.

Ask the children to help you set out the pet shop. Make a price list for the various items. Discuss why fish tanks could not be made from boxes (because of the need for transparency). Ask the children to bring from home any fish tanks they might have for the shop. Let the children cut out some fish shapes and attach these by wool to a cardboard lid. Turning the lid will make the fish look as if they are swimming.

Discussion

Do all pets need the same food? Should the animal homes be different shapes and sizes? Why? What else do pets need apart from food and shelter? What sorts of things are sold in a pet shop?

Finding out

Chapter four

Young children are naturally inquisitive and from babyhood will have spent much of their time investigating the world around them. It is very easy, therefore, to extend the child's naturally occurring investigations into slightly more formal classroom activities.

The activities, as always, must have a practical base and much thought must be given to classroom management to enable this to happen. The activities suggested are all based on familiar materials and ideas and all take place in or around school.

In technology, it is important to make sure that wherever possible children make discoveries about the properties of materials and then are led to think how these materials are used commercially to our advantage. It is for this reason that, for instance, in the activity 'About colour' where children have been mixing colour and watching colour being separated, the children's attention is then drawn to a commercial paint chart and they are asked to think about paints and dyes used in the home and in clothing. Similarly, after an investigation into mirrors, the children are asked to look at wing mirrors on the cars in the car park and to consider why they are used.

About sounds

Objective
To investigate the sounds made by a 'sounds robot'.

What you need
Two grocery boxes (one smaller than the other), scissors, adhesive, beads, buttons, ring-pulls, paper-clips, wool, fur fabric, paper plates, a metal spoon, a wooden spoon, straws, cardboard, long cardboard tubes, tape-recorder, blank tape.

What to do
Cut a rectangle from each of two sides of the large grocery box, cutting from the top (Figure 1). Stick a smaller box on the top to form the head of the robot. Ask the children to help cover the robot by sticking various items to it. These could include beads, buttons, ring-pulls, paper-clips, wool and fur fabric. Ask the children to suggest what might be

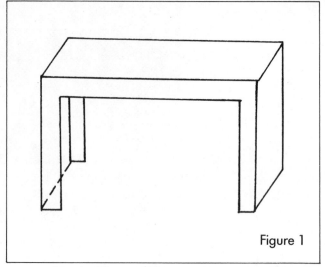

Figure 1

suitable for facial features (for example, paper plates for eyes and fur fabric for hair).

Each day put out a different striking instrument (such as a metal spoon, a wooden spoon, straws or a piece of cardboard) and ask the children to use it to tap on the different items with which the robot has been covered. Encourage them to listen to the different sounds made by the robot as the striker scrapes or taps it.

Follow-up

Let the children take turns to stand behind the robot and speak through a long cardboard tube, pointing the tube at someone in front of the robot. Ask the child standing in front to try to reply.

Give a group of children a long cardboard tube each and make a tape recording of them speaking in their 'robot voices'. They could also sing or say rhymes. Play the recording back to them and see if they can identify each other's voices.

Discussion

Can you move around like a robot? What part of the robot made the loudest sound? Was that part always the loudest whatever striker was used?

About paper

Objective

To find out some of the properties of paper.

What you need

Two pieces of plain white paper for each child, various sorts of paper such as tissue paper, sugar paper, brown wrapping paper, string, a weight, cardboard, crayons, pipette or contact lens cleaner container, newspaper, adhesive.

What to do

● Give each child in the group a piece of plain white paper. Ask each child in turn to try to make a different sound with the paper (such as scrunching, flicking, wafting, tearing). Give each child a second piece of paper to repeat all the different noises made during the game.

● Test the strength of different sorts of paper. Make a hole in each piece of paper and tie a piece of string through it. Suspend a weight from each piece of paper in turn. Ask the children to predict whether the paper will tear. Repeat this experiment using two pieces of paper stuck together. Repeat it again using cardboard and then soak the cardboard in water and let the children see the layers of paper come apart.
● Colour a small piece of sugar paper thickly with wax crayon, then drip some water using a pipette or contact lens cleaner container on to the waxed paper and on to a piece of unwaxed sugar paper. Ask the children to describe what happens to each piece of paper.
● Give the children some pieces of rolled-up newspaper and ask them to make something with it. Ask them to notice whether the paper bends or tears as they use it.

Discussion

How many different sounds did we make with the paper? Which paper was the strongest when we suspended a weight from it? Which tore straight away? What would we use the strong paper for? Why do you think cardboard is so strong? What do we use it for?

About wet and dry

Objective
To investigate the effect of water on different substances and materials.

What you need
One bowl of wet sand, one bowl of dry sand, paper, felt-tipped pen, sand tray, sand-play toys such as moulds and a sand wheel, one bowl of wet soil, one bowl of dry soil, waterproof clothes, sponge, umbrella, water tray.

What to do
Show the children two bowls of sand, one which is wet and one which is dry.

Ask the children to compare the two bowls of sand, first by looking and then by feeling the sand. Make a list of words the children use to describe the sand and display it near the sand-play area.

Ask some of the children to pick up each bowl carefully and tell the other children which bowl is heavier and which bowl is lighter. Ask the children to tell you why they think one bowl is heavier and what they think it might contain which the other bowl does not.

Let two or three children play with sand toys, first in the dry sand, then swapping to the wet sand. Ask them to tell the other children in the group which toys were best in the wet sand (such as moulds) and which were best in the dry sand (such as sand wheels). Allow all the children plenty of free play with both sorts of sand.

On another day show the children two bowls of soil, one wet and one dry, and ask them to examine and compare as they did with the sand. Make sure the children wash their hands after handling the soil. Discuss how the rain makes soil wet and is needed for plants to grow. Older children could discuss the difficulties experienced in countries where there is too much or too little rain.

Make a collection of waterproof clothes and an umbrella. Pour a little water on to the various waterproof materials and discuss what happens. As a contrast, place a sponge in the water tray and ask the children to watch carefully and describe what happens. Ask the children to compare the sponge before and after it soaks up the water.

Discussion
What were your hands like after you had played in the dry sand? What about after you had played in the wet sand? What happens to an indoor plant if you forget to water it? What do we use to soak up spills?

About colour

Objective
To investigate natural and commercially produced colours.

What you need
Paints, paint palettes, leaves, paint colour chart, blotting or sugar paper, felt-tipped pens, beetroot, saucepan, white cotton fabric, biscuits, icing sugar, food colouring.

What to do
The following activities should take place over several sessions.
● In one session ask the children to paint pictures, mixing the colours freely on a palette. In a second session give each child a palette or dish containing two colours which can be mixed to form a new colour (such as yellow and blue to form green or yellow and red to form orange) and three leaves. Ask the children to paint a leaf with each colour and to make leaf prints. Ask the children then to mix the two colours on their palette and paint the new colour on to the third leaf and make some more prints.

Ask the children to look at each other's prints and find out which colours were a mixture of the two original colours. Show the children a commercially produced household paint card and discuss how the various colours and shades might be mixed.
● Give the children a piece of blotting paper (or sugar paper) each and a felt-tipped pen. Ask each child to make a mark on the paper and then watch the colour from the pen change as it is absorbed through the paper. Encourage the children to look at each other's paper and describe what has happened. Swap over so that the children each try several colours.

● Show the children a beetroot (if possible still with roots and stalk) and discuss how it is part of a plant which grows under the ground. Peel and boil the beetroot. Discuss the difference in colour of the water before and after boiling the beetroot. Dip a piece of white cotton material into the water and discuss with the children the change which has occurred.
● Ask the children to help you to ice some plain biscuits. Make up some white icing by mixing icing sugar and a few drops of water. Ask the children to help

to stir the icing to the right consistency, then add a few drops of food colouring and mix again. Let each child ice his own biscuit.

Discussion

Which colours did you like in the leaf prints? Do you have any colours at home which are on the paint chart? How many colours did you see on the paper from one felt-tipped pen? Did you like the colour the beetroot made? Do you have any clothes which have been dyed bright colours? Who do you think dyes the cloth?

About bubbles

Objectives

To investigate bubbles and think about their commercial use.

What you need

Fizzy lemonade, plastic cups, several bowls of water, washing-up liquid, commercially produced bubble mixture or home-made mixture (containing one part glycerine, three parts washing-up liquid, three parts water), florist's wire or commercially made 'bubble blowers', powder paint, paper, straws.

What to do

This activity is suitable for outdoors, on a warm day.

Ask the children to sit on the grass and tell them that, as a special treat, they are to have a drink of fizzy lemonade. Show the children the bottle and ask them whether they can tell it is fizzy or whether it just looks like water. Shake the bottle gently so that the bubbles are visible and

ask the children to describe what is happening. Ask the children to listen carefully for the 'fizz' and watch the bubbles as you open the bottle. Pour a small amount of lemonade into a cup for each child and, as they taste it, ask whether they can feel the bubbles on their tongues.

When the children have finished their drinks, ask them to wash their own cups by first washing them in a bowl of water to which they have watched you add some washing-up liquid, and then rinsing in a second bowl of clear water.

Tell the children that they are now going to play with some bubbles. Give small groups of children a bowl of water and add some washing-up liquid, then let the children mix the water to form bubbles. Let them play with the bubbles. Provide the groups with a commercially produced bubble mixture or a mixture of water, washing-up liquid and glycerine. The children could either use commercially produced 'blowers' or home-made ones made by making a loop at the end of thin florist's wire. Encourage them to make bubbles of different sizes and to experiment with different ways in which to make bubbles,

About changes in cooking

Objective
To observe changes which occur during cooking.

What you need
Bread, electric toaster, two packets of jelly, water, jug, jelly mould, electric kettle, equal weights of raspberries and sugar, saucepan, cooker, saucer, vegetables, knife, two vegetable stock cubes, food blender or liquidiser, word processor (optional).

What to do
Tell the children that during the next few days they are going to help to do some cooking, and that each time they are going to watch carefully for any changes that may occur in the food that is cooked.
● Give each child in the small group a piece of bread and discuss what it looks like, how it feels and whether it has a smell. Let them taste a small piece of the bread. Show the children a toaster and explain simply how it will become hot and how careful they must be when using

such as by blowing or by waving the 'blowers' in the air. Allow the children to make bubble prints. Mix some powder paint thinly in a paint pot and add a generous squirt of washing-up liquid. Let the children blow into the mixture with drinking straws until the mixture bubbles to the top of the paint pot. Add more washing-up liquid if necessary.

Ask the children to place a piece of paper on to the bubbles to make the print.

Discussion
Who makes the bottles of lemonade? Why do you think they put bubbles into it? Have you seen someone at home using washing-up liquid? Where is it bought from? If we blow bubbles through a square loop, will we get square bubbles?

it. Toast the bread, then ask the children to compare the toasted and untoasted bread.

● Show the children a packet of jelly. Take out the jelly and discuss its colour, size, texture and smell. Give each child a small piece to taste. Make up a second jelly, asking the children to observe carefully how it dissolves in the water. Make a third comparison later when the jelly has set.

● Show the children some raspberries and explain that they are going to make jam with them. Discuss the colour, shape and smell of the fruit. Boil the raspberries until the juice runs out. Discuss how the fruit has changed. Add the same weight of sugar and boil for a further three minutes. Put a little of the jam on a saucer so that the children can see how the mixture has thickened and set.

● Make vegetable soup, beginning by showing the children the vegetables (for example two onions, two carrots, one swede, a few sprouts and two courgettes) and discussing their size, colour, shape and texture. Peel and boil the vegetables (adding two vegetable stock cubes to the water) until they are soft. Let the children see how the vegetables have changed and become soft. Blend the vegetables to make a soup and discuss the way the vegetables have now become a thick liquid.

Follow-up

Ask the children to choose one of the recipes which have been used during the last few weeks. Ask them to describe the cooking process and let them dictate while you type the recipe on a word processor. Ask the children to illustrate their recipe by drawing the ingredients that were used as well as the finished product.

Discussion

Did all the ingredients in our cooking change in some way? Were all the ingredients hot or cold at the beginning? Were they hot or cold at the end? What do you think made the ingredients change?

About light

Objective

To find out about natural and electrical light sources.

What you need

Torches, television, computer, cardboard tubes, coloured acetate film, coloured tissue paper, black sugar paper, one piece of coloured sugar paper, adhesive or elastic bands, scissors.

What to do

Take the children outside and discuss why it is light (avoid looking directly at the sun). Discuss how street lamps, car headlights and moonlight all help us to see at night-time. Go back into school and walk around the building looking for dark places and light places. Ask the children to tell you why the various places are lighter or darker. Look for windows, doorways or electric lighting which affect the lightness or darkness.

If possible, take a small group of children to a stock room where there are no windows. Go inside the room and shut the door, reassuring the children that you are going to turn on a light quickly. Shine a torch around the room, asking the children to tell you what they can see in its beam. Turn the electric light on and ask them whether they can see more clearly. Discuss why it was so dark.

Back in the classroom, let the children turn a torch on and off. Open the torch so that the children can see the batteries which give the power source. Turn on a television and computer which have a light to show that they are turned on. Notice also the light from the screens when the appliances are on.

Ask the children to cover one end of a cardboard tube with a piece of coloured acetate film. Let them secure the film with adhesive or an elastic band (Figure 1). Discuss how when they look through the cylinder everything looks coloured.

Cut out any simple shape from the middle of a piece of black sugar paper. Place a piece of coloured acetate film behind it and hold it up to the window. Replace the film with a piece of coloured sugar paper. Ask the children which looks the prettiest and discuss how the light shines through the acetate film.

Ask the children to fold and cut snowflake shapes from a piece of black sugar paper (younger children will need help with cutting) and stick a piece of coloured tissue paper behind the black.

Stick the snowflakes to the window. Make some more snowflakes using coloured acetate film instead of tissue paper. Place them against the window when the sun is shining directly through and they may throw coloured reflections on to the floor.

Discussion

What was the darkest place in school? Why was it so dark? Is it lighter outside on a sunny day? Does the television or computer have to be plugged in before it can be switched on? Do you know that you should never touch a plug or a socket unless an adult is there to help you? Why?

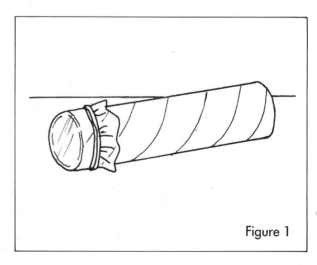

Figure 1

About mirrors

Objective
To find out about mirrors and their uses.

What you need
A large mirror, a small mirror for each child, access to the school car park, paper, crayons.

What to do
Group the children in front of a large mirror (a children's full length unbreakable mirror which is free-standing would be the best and safest — they are available from educational suppliers). Ask one child to sit in front of the other children facing the mirror. Ask the children to take it in turns to make a movement or gesture such as standing up or raising an arm. Let the child sitting in front of the others describe what they are doing. Discuss how the child sitting at the front can see what is happening behind her because she is looking at the others in the mirror. Let the children take turns at being the person at the front.

Give each child a small mirror and ask them to sit with their back to the large mirror, positioning the small mirror so that they can see the large mirror in it. Ask them what they can see.

Take the children outside to the car park. Ask them why they think every car has a mirror on the side.

Follow-up
Ask the children to look at themselves in a small mirror and draw, as carefully as they can, what they see. Ask them to look in the mirror at their faces when they are smiling, looking sad and looking angry.

Discussion
If the large mirror was not there, could you have seen what was happening behind you? Why do drivers need a mirror at the side of their vehicles? Is there a mirror inside the vehicle? Have you ever seen a mirror near the stairs of a bus or in a shop? Why do you think it might be there?

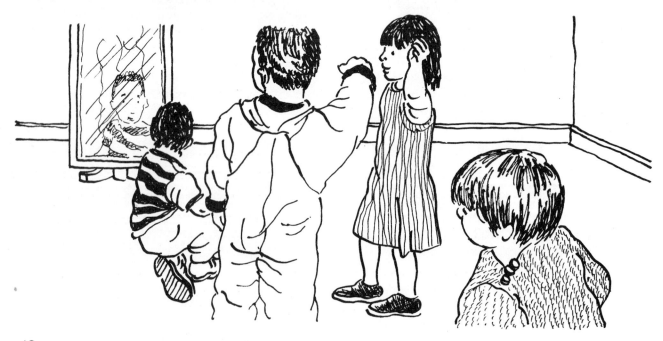

Out and about

Chapter five

Evidence of technological development is all around us, and through the activities in this chapter, children will begin to appreciate that development.

The suggested activities take place in the context of outdoor environments. The children will be led to consider why two different areas, a rural area and a town area, have developed in particular ways. They will also think about the nature of a leisure area and the structure of children's playground equipment. They will begin to appreciate the natural world around them as they study the weather and soil. Through recording the weather, the children are introduced to simple and practical apparatus, the purpose of which they will readily understand.

Throughout these activities, the children will have opportunities to work in groups and individually, to communicate their ideas and findings, to use and handle various materials and to use the computer to make a class book.

Comparing places

Objective
To make children aware of the physical differences between environments and of their purpose.

What you need
Transport to nearby town and country environments, photocopier paper, pens, card, Plasticine, pencils, crayons, adhesive, a copy of *Town Mouse and Country Mouse* by Annie McKie (Ladybird).

What to do
Arrange a visit to two different types of environment, in the country and in a town. You will probably need to take the children in cars or a bus to the two locations and take them for a short walk at each.

In the town, ask the children to look out for houses, different types of shops, commercial buildings, a church, police station or factory, as well as pelican crossings, traffic lights and post boxes. Plan the route carefully so that parking, if applicable, is not a problem, and children see as much as possible in a short time. The country walk should enable the children to see some aspect of farming or wildlife or both.

Discuss the differences in appearance, in purpose and in the sounds which can be heard in each area.

Back in the classroom, draw and photocopy a simple road layout. On a separate piece of paper, draw and photocopy appropriate items seen on your visit such as shops, houses, traffic lights, factories, animals, trees, ponds, crops, farm buildings. Give each child a copy of each piece of paper. Ask the children to cut out the various items and arrange them on the road layout in suitable places. Encourage the children to move their pictures about until everything fits and is in an appropriate place, before sticking them to the base layout.

Give each child a small square of card on which to make a picture out of Plasticine of one item he has seen on the walk. In groups, encourage the children to look at each other's Plasticine pictures and sort them into 'town' and 'country' sets. Put the squares of card together on a table to build up a town and country picture. Read *Town Mouse and Country Mouse* with the children.

Discussion

What did you like best about our town visit and what did you like best about our country visit? Were there more people in the town or in the country? Was it noisy or quiet? Who works in the town? Who works in the country? When do you go to the town? When do you go to the country?

A street model

Objective

To help the children to consolidate what they have learned about a town or village environment.

What you need

A variety of boxes such as shoeboxes and cereal packets, brightly coloured paper, scissors, small cardboard tubes, a large piece of paper such as a strip of wallpaper, pencils, crayons, adhesive, construction toys such as DUPLO or Mobilo, four teddy bears, tape recorder and blank tape.

What to do

Explain to the children that they are going to help to make a model road with buildings such as houses and shops on each side. Ask each child to choose a box and to cut pieces of paper to the right size and then to stick one on to each side of the box. Ask them to cut triangular pieces of paper, then stick them to the top of one side of the box to represent the roof. Let the children make windows and doors out of coloured paper and stick them on to the buildings, according to their own designs.

On a long sheet of paper, draw and colour a road, and ask the children to place their models along it. Discuss whether all the shops should be placed together, or spaced out between the houses.

Discuss what notices or road signs might be suitable. For example, the children might suggest a notice asking drivers to drive carefully, or a 'shop here' sign near the shops. Let the children make appropriate notices, either writing them themselves or with an adult acting as scribe. The notices can be stuck to small cardboard tubes and placed in appropriate positions along the road.

Let the children make vehicles for the model street, using construction toys.

Follow-up

Use the model road to help you tell a story. For example, make up a story about a child who goes to the shops with his mum or dad in one of the model vehicles. He has four teddies with him, but when he gets to the greengrocers he only has three teddies. He goes back to the car and finds the fourth teddy on the seat. Four teddies are hard to carry so he puts two in his shopping bag and carries two. At each stage of the story, count the teddies, making the story into a counting exercise as well as reinforcing work on 'the street'. Let the children help to make up the story by choosing which shops the boy goes to and who he sees in the town.

Tape record the story, so that it can be repeated, with children holding up the correct number of teddies at appropriate times.

Discussion

Who do you think might live in our model street? Who might work there? Who might visit the street and why?

In the park

Objective

To encourage children to evaluate their local park or play area.

What you need

Access to a local park or play area, protective gloves, polythene bags, pencils, crayons, paper.

What to do

Take a group of children to the local park or play area and allow them time to play on swings, climbing frames and slides. Walk round the park, encouraging the children to look and talk about what they see.

Ask the children to stand at the side of the play area and make some observations about the facilities. Look for anything which might spoil the area, such as litter, or which might be dangerous,

such as broken glass. Ask the children to put on protective gloves and help pick up pieces of litter (but not broken glass), and put it in polythene bags to take to a litter bin.

Look for litter bins in which to deposit the litter, and consider whether there are enough of them and whether they are well placed. Discuss whether it would be possible to have a special area for dogs.

Ask the children to notice anything which may have been done to make the area especially pleasant such as the planting of flowers, shrubs or trees, the placing of fountains or statues or the placing of benches for people to sit on.

Back in the classroom, ask the children to draw as much as they can remember of the visit. After discussion about the visit ask them to draw the ideal play area. Compare the facilities in the two sets of pictures. Discuss what improvements could be made.

Discussion

Do you think everybody should help to take care of the park? How could you help to take care of it? Should we write a letter to someone who works for the park asking them to plant more flowers or to put more litter bins in the park?

Slides

Objective

To find out about the physical characteristics of a slide.

What you need

A PE bench and two PE boxes, pieces of cloth, foam-backed carpet, polythene, a cork tile or mat, talcum powder, furniture polish, duster, boxes, stiff card, paint and adhesive (optional).

What to do

Ask the children to describe a slide in a children's playground. Encourage them to talk about the steps leading up to the top, the slide and the supports.

Show the children the PE bench and a box and ask them how they could be made into a slide. Prop the bench safely on to the box, then ask the children to take turns at sliding down. Next, ask each child to choose a piece of material (such

53

as cloth, foam-backed carpet, polythene or cork) to sit on as they slide down. As each child slides down, ask them to tell the other children how it feels and whether it makes them slide down faster or more slowly. Some children may notice that rubber soled shoes slow them down.

Sprinkle the PE bench with talcum powder and let the children test whether the slide is slippier. Repeat the test after polishing the slide, and after putting the slide at a higher angle, either by using another PE box, or by turning the original box on to a different side.

Follow-up

Ask the children to choose boxes to make into a model slide. Use boxes for the steps and support, and stiff card for the slide. Let the children stick their model together when they are satisfied with the design. When the adhesive is dry, let the children paint the model.

Discussion

Do you like to go on slides that are very high, or just a bit high? Why? Have you ever been on a slide which is still damp after the rain? Did you slide down quickly or slowly when the slide was damp? Which things made the PE bench into a fast slide? Which things made the slide slower? What makes a slide strong? Why does it need to be strong?

Swings

Objective

To find the best materials to make a model swing.

What you need

Cotton, wool, string, weights, teddy bears, rectangles of paper, card, cork and wood, construction toys (such as Gymbo, Quadro, Junior Meccano), adhesive tape, garden cane or broom handle, two chairs.

What to do

Before the activity ask each child to bring a teddy bear to school. Make sure you have a few spares for children who do not manage to do this.

Ask the children to describe a swing and discuss the frame and the moving parts. Tell the children they are going to make a model swing that must be the right size for their teddy and strong enough to hold his weight.

Help the children to tie a weight to various threads such as cotton, wool and string and then see which of them are strong enough to hold the weight without breaking. Ask the children why a thread which snaps would not be good for their teddy's swing. Ask them to choose a strong thread for the swing.

Next ask the children to choose a strong seat for the swing. Ask them to test the strength of various materials that could be used for the seat either by placing a weight on the rectangles of thin paper, thicker paper, card, cork or wood and lifting them up, or by trying to tear each of the rectangles.

Ask the children to look at the size of the teddy before they begin to construct the frame of the swing. The children can use construction toys such as Gymbo, Quadro or Junior Meccano for the frame. Give the children any help needed in constructing the frame, in tying the thread and seat in position or in using adhesive tape, but let them follow through their own ideas as far as possible. The children will also need to be given time to make alterations if the first model does not work.

Let the children put the teddy on the swing and play with it. Ask the children whether they think the length of the thread on their model swing makes any difference to the teddy's ride.

Let the children watch while you set up two pendulums. Suspend a weight from a short piece of string and tie the string to a cane or broom handle, placed between two chairs. Make another pendulum using a long piece of string. Ask the children to watch carefully when the two pendulums are set in motion together.

Discussion

Was your swing big enough for your teddy to sit on? Was it strong and firm? Did it stand up easily?

Climbing frames

Objective

To think about the structure of climbing frames.

What you need

Access to a PE or nursery climbing frame, construction toys such as Mobilo or Gymbo, paper, pencils, crayons, rolled-up newspaper, adhesive tape.

What to do

Discuss the climbing frames which the children have been on in the park. Ask them to describe the shape of the climbing frames and what they might have been made of.

Take the children to look at the PE climbing frame or the nursery climbing frame. Ask the children to describe the design and material.

Ask the children each to make a model climbing frame out of construction toys.

As they proceed with the activity, point out any particularly good designs which have a firm, wide base. When they have made their models, let the children make an observational drawing of their own model.

Give the children several pieces of rolled-up newspaper and ask them to work with a partner to make another model climbing frame. Encourage the children to construct a wide base which can stand up, before adding to the height. Help them to apply adhesive tape if necessary.

Discussion

When you climbed on the climbing frame, did you already know that it would be strong enough to hold you? What would have happened if it had wobbled and bent while you were on it? Do you think your model climbing frame was as strong as a real one? Would it be strong enough for a doll or a teddy to play on?

Recording the weather — rainfall

Objective

To compare amounts of rainfall over a period of time and to be able to understand a very simple rain gauge.

What you need

Spade, two plastic bottles, a bucket (partly filled with sand or gravel), a plastic funnel, different coloured elastic bands, felt-tipped pens, waterproof clothing and a pipette or a syringe (optional).

What to do

Dig a fairly shallow hole in the ground. Place the bucket, partly filled with gravel, in the hole. (This should ensure that it remains in place.) Push a plastic bottle into the sand or gravel in the bucket and place a funnel in the top of the bottle to collect the rain.

Take groups of children outside at regular intervals over a period of time to see how much rain has fallen into the bottle. Pour the rain-water from the bottle outside into another plastic bottle, which can then be taken into the classroom. Ask the group of children to show the rest of the class the bottle of rain-water. Ask one of the children to place a coloured elastic band round the bottle showing where the rain-water comes to. Tip the water away but leave the coloured band on the bottle so that the level on the following days or weeks can be compared.

Ask the children to fill in a chart, as in Figure 1, by drawing the coloured band on the picture of the bottle. Use a different coloured marker on the bottle and the chart on each reading so that comparisons can be made quite easily.

How much rainfall was there each week?

Monday 1st week	Monday 2nd week	Monday 3rd week	Monday 4th week	Monday 5th week
			none	

Figure 1

Follow-up

Make a collection of rainy day clothes. Test for waterproofing by asking a child to model the clothes and dripping water on to them using a pipette or syringe.

Discussion

Can you tell from the chart which week or day had the most rain? Were there any times when no rain fell at all? Do you like the rain? What is the rain good for?

Recording the weather – sunshine

Objective

To observe sunshine and shadows and to record observations.

What you need

Chalk, paper, pencils, computer and concept keyboard (optional).

What to do

Take the children outside several times so that they can see the correlation between sunshine and shadows. Let them chase each other's shadows and notice how many things make shadows on sunny days but not on cloudy days.

Take a group of children outside to a tarmac or concrete area and draw round the children's shadows using chalk. Repeat this at the same time each day and back in the classroom ask the children to report to the rest of the class whether a shadow could be drawn.

Ask the children to fill in charts, using Figure 1 for reference, by drawing their shadow and a sun if they were able to see their shadows, or by leaving the space blank if there was no shadow.

Shadows could also be drawn at different times on the same day, to show the movement of the sun. Take the children outside and draw round their feet with chalk on the playground. Let the children write their names in the feet outlines. Demonstrate the movement of the sun by asking them to stand in the

Sunshine Chart

Monday	Tuesday	Wednesday	Thursday	Friday
sun	no sun	sun	no sun	no sun

Figure 1

same position at various times during the day as you draw their shadows.

difference in the shape of your shadow at different times of the day? When was it biggest? When was it smallest?

Follow-up

Make an overlay for the concept keyboard, and write one sentence, 'Today the weather is . . .' and draw pictures depicting the sun, clouds, two thermometers, rain and wind. Write the words 'sunny, cloudy, warm, cold, rainy, windy' under the appropriate pictures. Each day or each week (depending on how often you wish to make weather recordings), let a child press the sentence and the right picture(s). The print-outs can gradually be built up to make a class book about the weather. Children could add their own pictures to accompany the print-outs. Alternatively, enough print-outs could be made each day/week for the children each to have their own books about the weather.

Discussion

Do you like sunny days? How often is it sunny, according to our chart? Have you seen the television weather news? What is the symbol for sunshine on the television? Why do you think people might want to know what the weather is going to be like? Was there much

58

Recording the weather – temperature

Objective
To become aware of temperature and begin to use a thermometer.

What you need
Two large thermometers, a bucket (partly filled with sand or gravel), coloured elastic bands, pencil, a collection of clothes suitable for different temperatures (optional).

What to do
Place a large thermometer in a bucket, partly filled with sand or gravel, and leave the bucket outside. Take a group of children outside at regular intervals to read the thermometer. Let the children note the temperature by placing a coloured elastic band round the thermometer according to the height of the mercury. Place a marker in the same position on a second thermometer to take back into the classroom. Ask the children to show the rest of the group where the marker is on that reading, and gradually make comparisons between markers (leave the markers on the thermometer). Get the children to fill in charts based on Figure 1 by drawing a line for the marker on to a picture of the thermometer. The children do not need to notice numbers; only that the marker is higher up on warmer days.

Follow-up
Make a collection of clothes suitable for different temperatures and discuss with the children why they are suitable.

Discussion
What does the thermometer tell us about the weather? Have you ever been poorly and felt too hot and had your temperature taken? Was that thermometer the same or different from the one we have used?

Class Temperature Chart				
Wednesday 1st week	Wednesday 2nd week	Wednesday 3rd week	Wednesday 4th week	Wednesday 5th week

Figure 1

Recording the weather – wind speed

Objective

To investigate wind speed and understand how we can use simple instruments to record it.

What you need

A piece of wood, a metal skewer, an eye dropper, a cork, a darning needle, two pieces of florist's wire, four miniature yoghurt pots, coloured adhesive paper circles, Blu-Tack, tray, commercial or home-made bubble mixture (optional).

What to do

Make a very light, freely moving anemometer in the following way. Hammer a metal skewer into a piece of wood for the base. For the top part, push the narrow end of an eye dropper into a cork. Make two holes right through the cork using a darning needle. Push two pieces of florist's wire through the holes in the cork. Push each of the four ends of the florist's wire through the base of the miniature yoghurt pots. Secure the wire inside the pot by bending or adding a small piece of Blu-tack. Attach the top to the base by placing the eye dropper over the metal skewer. Mark one of the pots with a coloured circle and place the anemometer on a tray which also has a coloured circle (Figure 1).

Take a group of children outside to measure the breeze or wind. Ask them to count how many times the coloured circle on the pot passes the one on the tray. This will help the children to notice whether it is turning quickly or slowly.

Back in the classroom ask the group of children to report their findings to the others. Ask the children to help fill in a

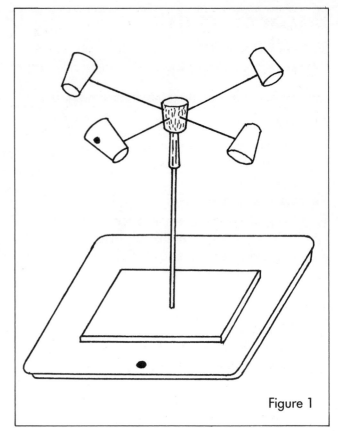

Figure 1

chart based on Figure 2 on page 61 opposite, stating that they could tell it was breezy, windy or calm because the anemometer turned slowly, quickly or not at all.

Follow-up

Take the children outside to see what happens to bubbles which are carried by the breeze or wind. Do this each time you take a reading with the anemometer so that the children can compare how the bubbles are blown in differing wind conditions.

Discussion

When the anemometer was turning slowly, what was happening to the trees, washing-lines or your clothes? What was happening to them when the anemometer was turning quickly? When did the bubbles get blown about the most?

Wind Chart

Friday 1st week	Friday 2nd week	Friday 3rd week	Friday 4th week	Friday 5th week
calm	windy	calm	breezy	windy

Figure 2

Recording the weather – wind direction

Objective
To look for evidence of wind direction and to make and use a simple instrument to record it.

What you need
A piece of wood, a metal skewer, an eye dropper, a cork, a fairly large feather, a variety of materials such as strips of paper, cloth, wool, paper plates, sticks or garden canes (optional).

What to do
Make a simple wind vane by using the same base as for the anemometer (a metal skewer hammered into a piece of wood). To make the top, push the narrow end of an eye dropper into a cork, then push the end of a large feather into the cork, as in Figure 1. Place the eye dropper over the skewer, to allow free movement of the wind vane.

Take a group of children outside and choose four easily identified features of the landscape, roughly equivalent to north, south, east and west. Place the wind vane in an open space and notice what part of the landscape it is pointing to and from. Use the same landmarks

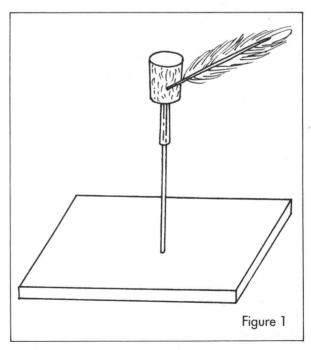

Figure 1

each time you take the weather vane outside so that the children will notice any change.

Back in the classroom, let the group of children tell the others where the feather was pointing. Using Figure 2 for reference, make a recording chart and ask a child to fill it in each time you take the weather vane outside, by drawing the landscape feature towards which the feather was pointing.

Follow-up

Offer the children a variety of materials, such as strips of paper, cloth, wool, paper plates, sticks or canes, so that they can make their own weather vanes. For example, they could choose to make a face out of a paper plate and stick on wool for hair, which will blow freely in the wind. They might make a flag or a streamer or a washing line between two sticks with paper cut-outs for washing. Take the children outside to test their weather vanes.

Discussion

Can you see the wind? Can you see what it does to things? What happens when you blow out a birthday candle? When you went outside with your own weather vanes, did they all blow the same way? Which way did the feather point? Was it the same every day?

Chart to show which way the wind is blowing				
Monday	Tuesday	Wednesday	Thursday	Friday

Figure 2

Know your soil

Objective
To begin to understand the importance of soil and what it is made of.

What you need
Access to school grounds, magnispectors, a bucket of sand, a bucket of clay, a bucket of compost, water, a jug or watering can, sand tray, sand toys, paint, varnish, crockery, cress, schizanthus or nasturtium seeds, plastic cups.

What to do
Take the children outside to look at the soil in the school grounds. Let them feel its texture, look at its colour and discuss what is growing in it (make sure they wash their hands after each activity). Put a little soil into several magnispectors and ask the children to look for minibeasts. Make sure you empty these back afterwards.

Show the children the three buckets containing sand, clay and compost and explain that soil is made up of a mixture of each. Pour a little water into each bucket so that the children can watch how it soaks into the sand and compost but stays on the top of the clay, at first, before beginning to soak in.

Back in the classroom explain to the children that they are going to use the sand, clay and compost.

Encourage the children to play with the sand, using it both wet and dry. Discuss the texture of the sand both wet and dry and which sand toys work best when it is wet and which are best when it is dry.

Tell the children that factories use sand mixed with other things to make glass. Look at the windows and talk about how they are transparent, unlike the sand.

Let each child use the clay to make a thumb pot. These can be dried on a warm window ledge or in an oven, then painted and varnished. Tell the children that crockery and pottery ornaments are made from clay.

Use the compost to plant some fast growing seeds such as cress or schizanthus (dwarf varieties make lovely indoor plants) or nasturtium which have interesting leaves. Plastic cups with holes drilled in the bottom make good plant pots. Explain to the children that the compost is the part of the soil made up from old leaves and other plants and living things which have rotted.

Follow-up
Make a class list of all the reasons why the children think soil is important, such as things which grow and live in it and things which can be made from it.

Discussion
Do you think soil looks the same everywhere? Is it more sandy at the seaside? Does it have more clay in it in some places? Do you know anyone who has a compost heap in their garden? What is it made from? Did you find any minibeasts in the soil samples? What did they look like?

Long ago

Chapter six

The activities in this chapter are designed to help children build up a concept of technological development over time.

Since young children are only able to understand what they experience, they find it difficult to visualise a world with less technology than there is today. The concept of time is also notoriously difficult for young children. They cannot easily differentiate between what happened one year ago and what happened 30 years ago.

When introducing the children to a sense of technological development, it is important to differentiate clearly between what was used in earlier times and what is used now.

It is also important that the activities are practical and enjoyable. The children will benefit greatly if adults of different generations can be drawn into the topics, by bringing in and explaining items or talking to the children about memories which may be relevant to the activities.

Transport

Objective
To find out about transport before the combustion engine and to think about a horse pulling a load.

What you need
Access to a road which is reasonably busy, pictures of horse-drawn transport and animals such as donkeys or camels carrying loads, a large cardboard box, a PE skipping rope, construction toys such as Mobilo, paper, pencils, crayons.

What to do
Visit the nearest main road. Ask the children to watch for cars, buses and lorries from a safe distance. Back in the classroom ask the children to draw what they have seen.

Show the children the large cardboard box and tell them that they are going to turn it into a horse and cart. Pretend that the cart has to carry a parcel from one house (one side of the room) to another house a long way away (another part of the room). Ask one child to be the horse and the other children to think how the horse is going to pull the cart. Using the children's suggestions as far as possible, and taking safety into consideration, fasten the rope, harness style, to the child and the box. The 'horse' can then crawl along, pulling the cart, perhaps with

another child taking on the role of driver.

Discuss how difficult it was for the child who was the horse to pull the heavy box and how much easier it might be to drive a car with an engine to do the work. Discuss in simple terms the disadvantage of modern transport regarding pollution of the environment.

Ask the children to draw pictures of themselves being a horse and pulling someone along in the cart.

Ask the children to make vehicles out of construction toys such as Mobilo. Let the children pull the vehicles apart, count the pieces and try to put them back together again in the same way as before, then in a different way.

Discussion
How do you come to school? Would a horse-drawn carriage make a different sound than a car? Which would be faster? What makes a car move? What would make a carriage move? Was it difficult pulling the 'cart'? How could it have been made easier?

Clothes

Objective
To consider children's clothes from earlier times to see how they have changed.

What you need
A collection of children's clothes and shoes, a collection of photographs brought in by the children, a collection of clothes adapted for role-play (optional).

What to do
Before the activity, ask the children to bring photographs of themselves and their parents and grandparents as children. Ask the staff to bring photographs of themselves as children. Compare the three sets of photographs, noticing the style of clothes and the photographs themselves. Some families may be able to produce very old sepia photographs of older generations. Display the photographs and encourage parents and staff to guess who the people are.

Ask the children to help you sort the clothes into sets — those for summer or winter, those for every day or best. Discuss why each set of clothes would be suitable for its purpose.

Follow-up
Make a collection of old-fashioned clothes for role-play. These could include old school hats or ties or gymslips. Clothes from jumble sales could be adapted to look old-fashioned.

Ask a parent or grandparent to visit and talk about their childhood, mentioning particularly their school and its facilities, and the games and toys that were available. Encourage the children to make comparisons with their own school.

Discussion
Were you surprised to see pictures of your parents and grandparents as children? Which clothes did you like best? Do you feel different when you wear the role-play clothes?

Household equipment

Objective

To compare and contrast past and present household equipment.

What you need

A collection of old-fashioned household equipment and modern equivalents, paper, pencils, crayons, a conventional oven, a microwave oven, a wooden spoon, an electric mixer, bowls and ingredients for making two cakes.

What to do

A visit to a Victorian museum, with a kitchen, would be an ideal starting point to this activity.

Ask the children's parents and grandparents to lend you any old-fashioned domestic items which they possess. Try to find modern equivalents.

Ask the children to describe, compare and contrast each pair of items. The items will differ, depending on what is available, but possible items could include irons, kitchen scales, hair curlers, radios or records. The differences will be in the design, material and weight although the purpose for each pair will be the same.

Ask the children whether they think that household equipment, machines or cars will change in the future. Ask them to draw what they think one of the items might look like in the future.

Ask the children to help to bake a cake, mixing the ingredients with a wooden spoon and baking it in a traditional oven. Borrow an electric mixer and microwave oven, and make a second cake. Share the cakes with the children and ask whether they both taste good. Discuss the time taken and what each cake looks and tastes like.

Discussion

Would you like to be able to use the old equipment or the modern equipment? Do you think it would have been easier or harder a long time ago? A lot of things we use today are run by electricity; do you think we use too much electricity? Do you think it matters if we use too much electricity?

Packaging

Objective

To help children become aware of the widespread use of packaging today, compared with former times.

What you need

A collection of packaged items such as cartons of milk or fruit juice, packets of cereals, rice, soap, boxes from toys or electrical goods, pictures of factories or machinery, brown paper sacks (from potatoes) and bags, small amounts of flour, sugar, rice and dried fruit, balance scales, greaseproof paper, spoons.

What to do

Ask the children to help to make a collection of packaged items. Explain that many factories are needed to make the cartons, boxes and bags and to package the goods. Show the children pictures of factories and machinery.

Tell the children that long ago many shops sold goods that were not packaged. Show the children items such as sugar, rice and dried fruit which would have arrived from other countries in big sacks and boxes and were weighed out for each customer.

Set up two shops and ask other adults to help groups of children in role-play. One shop should be a modern shop, using the packaged items. The second shop should be an old-fashioned shop where flour, sugar, rice and dried fruit are stored in large paper sacks (from potatoes) or any other large sack or bag that may be available to represent hessian sacks. Only small amounts of the goods need to go into the sacks. The 'shopkeeper' should weigh out small amounts of the goods using balance scales, before putting the goods into small paper bags for the 'customers'.

Follow-up

Depending on the age and experience of the children, discuss the convenience of modern packaging compared with the problem of using up too many raw materials. Encourage the children to consider what happens to packaging once we have finished with it.

Discussion

Do you think you would have enjoyed being a shopkeeper long ago? Would you have been good at weighing? Have you seen the shopkeeper in a greengrocer's weigh out your carrots or apples? Do you sometimes get carrots or apples in a packet?

Writing implements

Objective
To consider past and present methods of writing.

What you need
Pencils, crayons, felt-tipped pens, ballpoint pens, straight nib pens and ink, feathers, chalk, chalking boards, a box of damp sand, a stick, paper, several sets of rubber stamps, stapler, garden canes, adhesive (optional).

What to do
Ask the children to draw or write about their favourite school activities. Give groups of children different implements to use such as pencils, crayons, felt-tipped pens or chalk. Show the whole class the pictures and writing produced by each group. Observe the different designs of the implements and the colour and the thickness of line which they produce.

Tell the children that long ago people used very different methods of writing. Ask them to pretend to be in a time machine going back in time. Explain that at each stop, they will find children in school using different writing implements. Ask groups of children to try to draw or write using pen and ink, quill pens (using large feathers), chalk and chalking boards, and writing in damp sand with a stick. Explain that chalking boards were used before paper was plentiful. Explain also that teachers and children wrote in the sand, or on sandy soil outdoors, as in Biblical times.

Give each child a long piece of paper and ask them to draw a series of pictures or writing, then roll the paper into a scroll, sticking a small garden cane at each end. Explain that before books were made, writing was often put on to scrolls.

Follow-up
Let each group of children print a simple picture book. Ask each child to use one type of rubber stamp (for instance dinosaur stamps) to produce several pages, then another child to produce pictures of pets, and so on. Help the group to collate and staple together the pages to make several small picture books.

Discussion
What did you like best for writing and drawing? Which was easiest to use? Which was the hardest?

Art and craft

Chapter seven

Most children love to make things and it is important that their efforts should be genuinely valued by caring adults around them. Often, children bring into school items that they have made at home and these should be admired whether they have been made with a parent or entirely by the child.

In school, children should have many opportunities to be creative, without any teacher direction. Boxes, paper, wool and any other appropriate materials can be put out for the children to use with a choice of adhesive, adhesive tape, or paper-clips for fastening. It may well be worthwhile explaining this policy to parents so that they too will be ready to accept and value whatever the child takes home, even though to an adult's eyes it may not look like anything recognisable!

It is essential, however, that some activities should be teacher-directed so that children are free to concentrate on skills of either technique or design. Where early years children are given the opportunity to practise both technique and design, they may only be capable of concentrating on one. Thus, for instance, if a young child is asked to design a face for a puppet using a variety of materials, she may produce a good design, but end up with adhesive everywhere. On the other hand, the same child may make an excellent attempt at sticking when given all the parts of the face and asked to concentrate only on the sticking.

There will be times when, despite their limitations, children will be asked to design as well as make, and some will succeed in both. In short, the children should have many varied opportunities and circumstances in which to develop the skills of art and craft. This in turn will develop their design and technology capability.

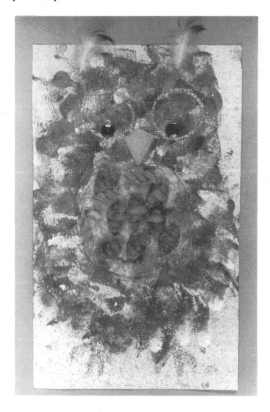

Bread printing

Objectives
To practise the techniques of printing, cutting and sticking.

What you need
A variety of loaves of bread (sliced, un-sliced, white, brown and wholemeal), bread rolls and fingers, a bread knife, sponges, paint, paper or card, indoor plant spray, brown paper circles, scissors, pasta, adhesive, silver pen.

What to do
Show the children the various sorts of bread, discussing similarities and differences. Cut the bread into slices and the rolls in half and get them to look at it again. Give each child a piece of bread.

Ask the children to dip a sponge into white, brown or orange paint and use it to apply paint to the bread. Let the children print with the bread on to paper. Ask them to leave any breadcrumbs that remain on the paper as this will add to the texture when the paint dries. Discuss with the children the differences in texture and pattern made by the different kinds of bread.

When the prints are dry, ask the children to cut carefully round them and arrange them on a circle of paper so that the effect produced is that of a plate of bread and butter. The children can stick the prints to the circle, using adhesive, when they are satisfied with the arrangement.

A simple but effective teacher-directed owl picture will give the children more practice in printing and sticking. Make the background by helping the children to spray the card with a thin paint mixture, using an indoor plant spray. When this is dry, draw a pencil outline of an owl or ask the children to draw their own

A feely dragon

Objective

To explore the textures of a variety of materials.

What you need

Large pieces of foam rubber or polystyrene packaging, a variety of items to stick to the dragon such as pasta, paper-clips, wool, small shells, foam pieces, beech nuts and silver foil, adhesive, red foil, two large shells, strips of card, plastic bubble packaging, descriptive word labels, food colouring, a clear jar with a lid, card.

What to do

Make a collection of items with different textures. Let the children feel and discuss the textures. Tell them that they are going to find out whether all the items will stick to polystyrene using adhesive.

outline. The children can then sponge-print the owl, using brown, white and orange paint, taking care not to put too much paint on to the sponge. When the paint is dry let the children draw circles for eyes with a silver pen and stick on sequins for the eye-centres, a triangle of paper for a beak and pasta for the body. Ask the children to take care in using adhesive, so that only a small amount is used.

Discussion

Were you very careful when you were printing with the bread? Do you like eating bread? Which is your favourite?

Explain that they are going to make a dragon from large pieces of foam rubber or polystyrene packaging. The head will be made from two pieces of packaging set at an angle, with red foil for the tongue, large shells for the eyes and wispy wool or nylon thread for smoke coming from the dragon's nostrils, while the rest of the body will be made up of segments of packaging pieces. Ask each child to stick a different set of items to each packing piece to make up parts of the body.

When they have finished sticking on the various objects, discuss with the children how well the adhesive has set, and re-stick some items if necessary using more adhesive.

Fasten the dragon to the wall by sticking two strips of card to the back of each packing piece and stapling them to the wall. Arrange the pieces in a long dragon shape, at child level.

Plastic bubble packaging makes an attractive background for such a display. Encourage the children to pop the bubbles and feel the different textures of the dragon.

Finish off the display by adding descriptive words such as 'smooth', 'lumpy', 'furry' or 'spiky'.

Follow-up

Colour some pasta shapes by putting a few drops of food colouring and a few drops of water into a clear jar with a lid. Add some pasta shapes then shake the jar. The pasta will quickly absorb the food colouring. Repeat this with different colours.

Allow the pasta to dry, then ask the children to design pasta pictures by sticking the pasta shapes firmly on to card using plenty of adhesive so that the pasta pictures can be touched. When the pictures are dry, ask the children to close their eyes and feel the pictures.

Discussion

Do you think the dragon is friendly? Which part is smooth, which part is spiky? When we coloured the pasta, where do you think the food colouring went? Could you tell your friend about your pasta picture by touching it and keeping your eyes closed?

Bright-eyed cat

Objectives

To develop techniques of colouring, colour sequencing, sticking and using string length for design.

What you need

Copies of photocopiable page 95, white card, scissors, green and red foil circles, strips of thin card, adhesive, long rectangles of card, crayons, wool, shoe box, bodkin, black paper, different coloured paper (including fluorescent colours) and foil, Blu-Tack.

What to do

Use photocopiable page 95 as a template to make a cat's head shape for each child. Ask the children to colour the head shapes with black crayon. Give

each child two circles of green foil, one circle of red foil and several thin strips of card for the eyes, mouth and whiskers (some children may be able to cut these shapes themselves). Ask the children to place the circles and strips in position on the cat's face, then carefully stick them in place, using only a small amount of adhesive. Next let the children use crayons to colour a rectangle of card for the cat's body. Encourage them to colour thickly in a colour sequence of their own choice.

To assemble the bright-eyed cat, thread a piece of wool on to a bodkin and knot the end. Push the bodkin through the card from the coloured side, arch the card and push the bodkin through the other end of the card from the underside, as in Figure 1. Make a knot in the wool on the coloured side on the cat's body, then allow the

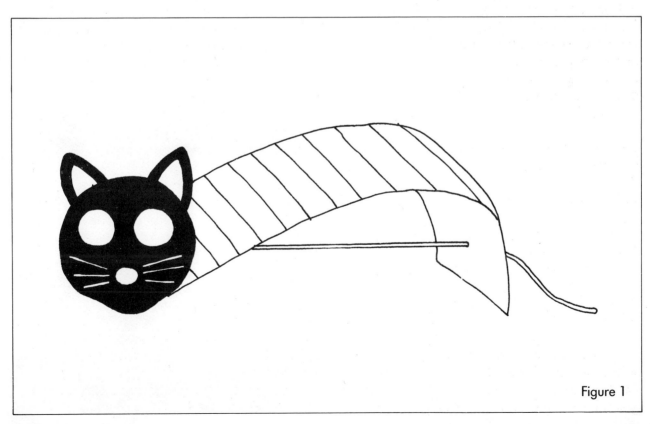

Figure 1

75

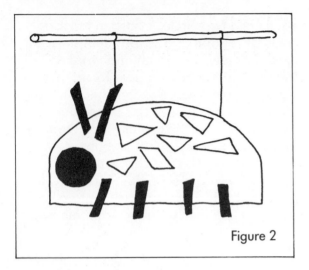

Figure 2

remainder of the string to dangle as a tail. Encourage each child to decide where the knot should be, depending on how long he wishes the tail to be and how arched the cat's back will become. Then let the children stick the cat's face to the front of the body, using plenty of adhesive (Figure 2).

Discuss how brightly the cat's eyes reflect, especially in darker areas of the room, and how real cats have eyes that reflect in the dark.

Follow-up

Line a shoe box with black paper and cut a small peep-hole in one end. Make several pinprick holes in the lid. Place several colours of paper, including foil and fluorescent paper, in turn at the opposite end to the peep-hole end, using Blu-Tack to hold them in place. Let the children discover which colours show up best in the dark.

Discussion

Have you ever seen a real cat make its back change shape so that it becomes really arched? Why do they do that? Have you ever seen a cat's eyes reflecting the light? Have you ever seen people wearing bright armbands on their sleeves? Why do you think they do that?

Free-choice puppets

Objective

To give the children an opportunity to try designing as well as making puppets.

What you need

Boxes, paper plates, cardboard cylinders, yoghurt pots, silver foil dishes, bottle tops, wool, pipe-cleaners, adhesive, adhesive tape, string, paint, socks, felt, scissors, fringed material or upholstery fringe, tapes of happy, sad or angry music, cassette recorder.

What to do

Explain to the children that they are going to make their own puppets. Put a collection of materials on to a table so that children can select what they want to use. Give the children a few ideas, such as using boxes or paper plates as bodies or heads, cardboard cylinders or pipe cleaners as legs and arms, or bottle tops, yoghurt pots or silver dishes as feet.

Let the children design and make their own puppets as far as possible, but help

may be needed with adhesive tape. In some cases tying parts together with wool, sticking or stapling would be appropriate. It is possible to turn boxes inside out to avoid brand names showing, by slitting down four sides of the box, turning them inside out and taping the sides together again.

Older children may wish to paint the puppets and this should be done carefully, reinforcing adhesive tape and fastenings where necessary. Younger children may find this difficult, but will be quite happy to leave the puppets un-painted.

When the children have made their puppets, attach strings to the top and hang the puppets up to display them. Encourage the children to make their puppets dance appropriately to happy and sad music such as *The Wand of Youth* by Edward Elgar and *Adagio* by Tomaso Albinoni, or they may enjoy angry music such as 'Mars' from Gustav Holst's *The Planet Suite*.

Follow-up

Let the children make a sock puppet. Prepare eyes, noses and tongues out of felt before the activity. Let the children practise putting their thumbs into the heel of the sock and their fingers into the toe before trying to sort out where the features should go. Encourage the children to place the features carefully on to the puppet and to use adhesive sparingly. Let them add hair made from wool or fringed material.

Let the children hold their dragon-like puppets while you read a story such as *There's No Such Thing as a Dragon* by Jack Kent (Blackie).

Discussion

Was it easy or difficult to decide how to fasten the parts of your puppet together? How many different ways did we do it?

String puppets

Objective

To let children design, make and use very simple string puppets.

What you need

Paper plates, brightly coloured material, silver foil dishes, a variety of materials such as coloured paper, foil, sequins, glitter, beads, conkers, wool and upholstery fringe, adhesive, scissors, stapler, string, indoor plant canes, a video of *Pinocchio*, black plastic bases from fizzy drinks bottles, black, brown and orange Vivelle (textured material, ideal for craft work).

What to do

Explain to the children that they are going to make a dancing clown puppet. Give each child a paper plate to use as the clown's face, then offer them a

variety of paper, wool, beads, sequins, glitter, conkers and fringe to be used for the clown's features and hair. Encourage them to be imaginative by using sequins and glitter on the face and hair, or perhaps using a bead or conker for the nose. Encourage the children to think carefully where to place features and hair, before sticking them in place. Explain that they should try to use the adhesive sparingly.

Let the children choose a piece of material for the clown's clothes, then staple it to the paper plate for them. Let the children make hats for their clowns by cutting out paper circles about the same size as the clown's face, then cutting a slit in the middle of the circle and pushing the plate through, securing it with adhesive tape. Ask them to stick a silver foil dish over the slit to complete the hat (Figure 1). Tape four strings to the

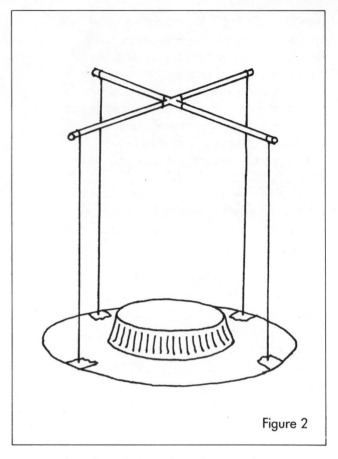

Figure 2

outside of each hat, then fasten each string at the top to two crossed-over indoor plant canes (Figure 2).

Encourage the children to play with their clowns in groups of two or three. Show them how to make the clowns dance sideways or backwards and forwards, jump over each other and so on.

Follow-up

Let the children watch a video of *Pinocchio*. Point out how Pinocchio is portrayed as a stringed puppet.

Let the children make walking minibeasts in the following way. Cut off the black plastic bases from fizzy drinks bottles and push the dents outwards to form a dome shape. Ask the children to cut out eyes, antennae, wings, spots and legs from black, brown and orange Vivelle, and stick them carefully on to the

Figure 1

plastic body. Make two holes in the back of the minibeast, then help the children to thread two pieces of string from underneath and fasten above to an indoor plant cane.

Show the children how to make their minibeast puppets move along the top of a table. Encourage them to make up stories about their puppets.

Discussion
Does your clown puppet look different from everybody else's? Were you pleased with it? What could you make your puppet do if it had strings fastened to legs and arms, like Pinocchio? Can you make your minibeast puppet look as if he is walking?

Making books

Objective
To give the children experience of different book shapes.

What you need
Two rectangular pieces of card (one slightly smaller than the other), adhesive, crayons, paint, sweet wrappers, coloured paper for collage work, another piece of rectangular card or paper for each child, for the second book (optional).

What to do
Ask the children to fold two rectangular pieces of card or paper (one slightly smaller than the other) as shown in Figure 1 and carefully apply adhesive to the central panels. This formation will allow illustrations on the two front flaps and the central panel as well as additional picture and writing sections on the inside of the two front flaps and the inner flaps.

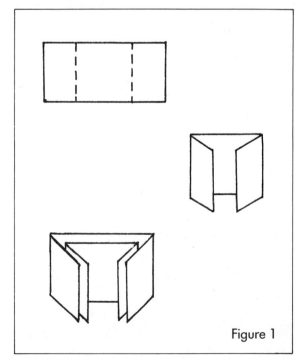

Figure 1

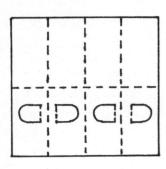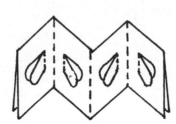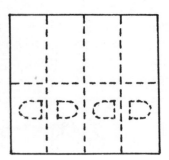

Figure 2

Many stories lend themselves to this book formation. For example, if the children know the story of Hansel and Gretel, ask them to draw or print several trees on the two front flaps, to represent the dark wood. Let them use the central panel to make a collage of the witch's house. Ask the children to re-tell the story by drawing and writing on the inside of the front flaps and on the two inner flaps. Alternatively, let the children draw or write the story on to separate pieces of paper which can later be stuck to the flaps.

Follow-up

Ask the children to help fold a rectangular piece of paper or card as illustrated in Figure 2, to form a concertina book with flaps. Let the children draw and write on the pages and under the flaps to illustrate stories such as one of the Spot books by Eric Hill.

Discussion

Do you have any books at home with flaps or windows? Do you have any pop-up books? Do you have any books with thick card pages rather than paper pages? Are all books the same size? Which are your favourite books? What do you like about them?

Working together

Chapter eight

As we all know, babies must totally rely on adults to supply all their needs. Early years children are only just beyond this stage and are still very reliant upon adult help and support. Love and care within a family or group must be experienced before the child can herself become a loving, caring member of that family or group. As the child grows through this stage, we can help her to become aware of the care she receives and the way in which adults act co-operatively, for the good of all.

Systems development in design and technology includes the interrelationship of people. This chapter illustrates activities where children and adults work as part of a group and highlights the benefits to be gained by such an approach. The activities take place in the context of home and business and industry.

Meals

Objective

To make children aware of the effort required when meals are provided for them.

What you need

Access to the school kitchen, miniature boxes of breakfast cereals, paper, adhesive, pencils, crayons, circles of paper, copies of photocopiable page 96, coloured card or paper.

What to do

Before the activity, make sure that none of the children suffer from allergies to cereals.

Begin by discussing with the children the various meals of the day, where they are eaten and who makes them.

Let the children taste various breakfast cereals, then help them to make a block graph showing their favourites. Stick the various packets in a line along the bottom of the paper. Ask the children to make a drawing of their own face, then cut it out and stick it above the packet of their favourite cereal.

Discuss school meals and what the children like to eat at school. Visit the school kitchen, if there is one, or take the children to see the lunches being prepared. Ask the children to form two lines: one of people who have school meals and one of those who eat packed lunches. Which line is longer?

Give each child a circle of paper to represent a plate. Ask them to draw a favourite meal on the plate. Ask the

Mark
Helen
CORN FLAKES

Juliet
MUESLI

David
Gina
Timothy
Claire
Rosanna
COCO RICE

Catherine
SUN BRAN

Robin
James
WEETYS

Meals for babies

Objective

To begin to understand how babies are cared for and how meals are carefully prepared and to observe changes which occur during cooking.

What you need

Several savoury and sweet tins of baby food, saucepans, cooker, tin opener, potato peeler, potatoes, carrots, bananas and apples, fork, one plastic spoon for each child, paper, pencils.

What to do

Before the activity, check that none of the children have food allergies.

Let the children watch as you open a savoury tin of baby food and heat it up. Give each child a spoonful of the food to taste. Discuss with the children the texture, smell and taste of the food.

children to show each other their favourite meals and tell each other what they are. Ask the children who prepares their meals. Do they ever help?

Distribute copies of photocopiable page 96 and ask the children to cut out the pictures and stick them to a piece of coloured card or paper to represent a place setting.

Discussion

Do you think some people work very hard to give you your meals? Where does the food come from before it is cooked? What has to be done after a meal? Do you sometimes help to wash up?

Peel and boil one or two potatoes and carrots, with the children watching from a safe distance. Discuss with the children the colours of the vegetables, inside and outside, and any colour changes which occur during cooking. Let them feel the hardness of the potatoes and carrots before cooking, and compare it with the softness after cooking. Mash up some cooked carrot and potato with a fork and give each child a spoonful of each to eat.

Help the children make a block graph showing whether they preferred the tinned or fresh food.

Repeat the process using a tin of sweet baby food and a mashed banana or cooked and mashed apple.

Discussion

Did you like all the baby food or just some of it? Why do babies need to eat food which is soft and mashed? Do you need to eat only soft food? What helps you to chew your food? Do you think people work very hard to look after babies? What else might they have to do?

Washing-up

Objective
To investigate the process of washing-up.

What you need
Two washing-up bowls, ready supply of water, washing-up liquid, enough saucers for the children to have one each, margarine, several tea towels, paper, pencils, crayons.

What to do
Discuss who does the washing-up at home and whether the children have ever helped. Explain that the children are going to do some washing-up, but first they are going to find out the best way to do it.

Set up two washing-up bowls, one with warm water and washing-up liquid, the other with warm water and no washing-up liquid. Lightly grease the saucers with a little margarine, then ask each child to wash a saucer at one of the two bowls. Let them compare the washed saucers and examine the water left in the bowls. Discuss with the children which water seemed the best for washing-up.

Add some washing-up liquid to the second bowl and let the children whose saucers are still greasy wash them again. Let the children dry the saucers and encourage them to observe what happens to the tea towels as the saucers become dry.

Repeat the activity using two bowls of cold water.

Using Figure 1 for reference, make some photocopiable recording sheets and ask the children to fill them in.

Ask the children to draw pictures of the people who wash up at home.

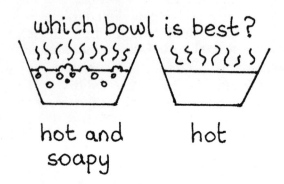

which bowl is best?

hot and soapy

hot

was cold water good or not good for washing a dish?

good for washing

not good for washing

Figure 1

Discussion

What water is best for washing-up? Do you think you would be allowed to help to wash up at home? Would someone at home be surprised that you know all about washing-up and which water is best? Where did the water go to when the saucers were dried? Where might you put the tea towel to dry?

Find a friend

Objective

To make children aware of the importance of friendship and co-operation when working or playing together.

What you need

Construction toys such as Mobilo, Stickle Bricks or building bricks, paper, crayons, pencils, twigs, vase, card, wool, adhesive tape, scissors, soil with ants, leaves, tree bark, a fish tank, a water tray or a larger tank, bread, honey, a piece of flower arranger's Oasis.

What to do

Help the children to form pairs, then ask each pair to make something together from a construction toy. Tell them that they must talk to each other first to decide what they are going to make. Encourage the children to keep talking and discussing the model as they work together, and to contribute equally to the work.

When the models are finished ask the pairs to draw what they have made and to write a caption together, describing it. Display the pictures drawn by each pair.

Cut some circles from card and on each one draw two smiley faces with the words 'We worked together'. Make some loops from wool and attach them to the backs of the circles with adhesive tape. Put some twigs in a vase, then hang the circles from the twigs. Over the course of a few days, write on the circles the names of any children who work well together. Display the vase by the children's drawings.

Follow-up

Illustrate further the concept of co-operation by allowing the children to observe how ants work together.

Collect some soil locally, with ants in, together with some leaves, tree bark or stone. Put them in a fish tank, and place this in a water-filled tray or larger tank to prevent the ants escaping. A piece of flower arranger's Oasis in the fish tank will provide the ants with shelter, into which they can burrow.

Put different sorts of food in the fish tank such as leaves on which there are aphids, or small pieces of bread and honey. Show the children how the ants work together to collect the food. Make sure that the ants are taken back to the place where they were found after a day or two.

Discussion

Is it easier to work together? How do the ants work together? Can you think of other people who have to work together?

The world of work

Objective
To help children understand that co-operation is needed in the world of work.

What you need
Access to a garage, paper, pencils, tools, foot-pumps, an old telephone and typewriter, empty paint and oil cans, pens and notepaper, construction toys, nursery go-karts.

What to do
Make arrangements to take the children to visit a garage where they will be able to see the mechanics working. If possible, ask one of the mechanics to explain what the others are doing and how they sometimes need to work together to get a job done. Allow the children plenty of time to look at the vehicles, tools and machinery being used.

Back in the classroom ask the children to draw as much as they can remember about the visit.

Set up a role-play garage. Where possible use real items such as foot-pumps, an old telephone, an old typewriter, empty paint and oil cans, pens and note books. Let the children make vehicles from construction toys such as Giant Engineer or Quadro. Some children might be able to lend their own go-karts.

Make a reception area and explain to the children that the customer, bringing a car in, has to be booked in by the receptionist before the car goes to the

working area. Explain also that the mechanic has to record the work he has done before the work is paid for.

Discussion

What did you see at the garage? Were the people there working together? In the play garage, can you sort out who will be the customer, the mechanic and the person at the desk? Can you all work well together?

The postman

Objective

To help children understand that the world of work provides us with many services.

What you need

Writing paper, envelopes, pens, a stamp, grocery boxes, red crêpe paper, Plasticine, brown wrapping-paper, string, scissors, adhesive tape, balance scales, book shelves, table, rubber stamps, postman's hat and bag.

What to do

Ask each child to bring an envelope and stamp to school. Ask each child to draw a picture or write a letter to another child. Make sure that each child will receive a letter. Help them to write the names and addresses on the letters and show them how to stick on a stamp. Take the children for a walk to the nearest post-box to post the letters and wait for the excitement when they arrive!

Back in school, discuss what will happen to the letters before they arrive back in school.

Set up a role-play post office and sorting office. Make a post-box by covering two grocery boxes with red crêpe paper. Stand the boxes on top of each other. Cut a hole in the top box so that letters can be posted.

Give the children a collection of empty boxes, brown paper (cut to different sizes), string, scissors and adhesive tape. Let the children wrap the boxes as parcels, putting Plasticine inside some to make them different weights. Arrange some book shelves or place grocery boxes on their sides to make different compartments for the sorting office. Let the children make pages of stamps, using rubber stamps.

Set up a table as the post office counter. Put plenty of envelopes and paper nearby so that the children can write each other letters to put in the post box. Let the children take it in turns to weigh parcels and sell stamps at the post office counter.

If possible, provide a postman's hat and bag. Let the children take turns at being the postman, emptying the post box and taking letters and parcels to the sorting office before delivering them to the right children.

Discussion

Does the postman often come to your house? Were you pleased to get a letter? How many people might have helped to get it to your house?

Hanging by a thread, see page 10

Incy Wincy spider needs a strong web to hang from. Can you find some strong materials?

these are weak

these are strong

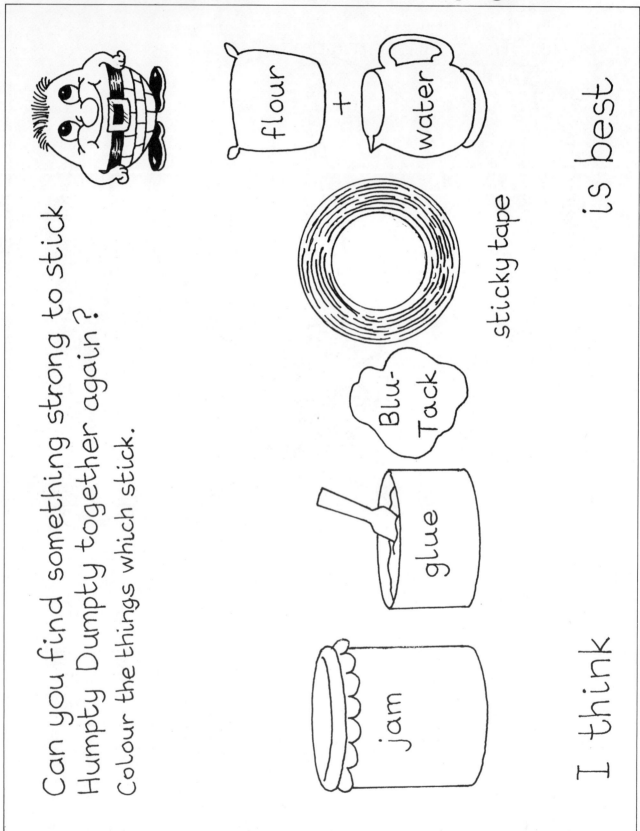

Can you find something strong to stick Humpty Dumpty together again?
Colour the things which stick.

flour + water

sticky tape

Blu-Tack

glue

jam

I think

is best

Swings and slides, see page 20

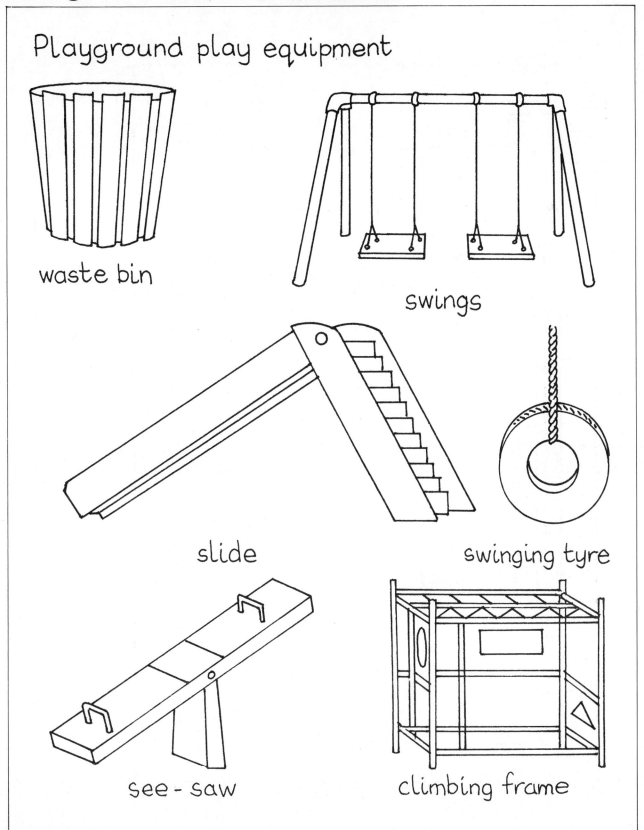

Playground play equipment

waste bin

swings

slide

swinging tyre

see - saw

climbing frame

The Shopping Basket, see page 27

Bright-eyed cat, see page 75

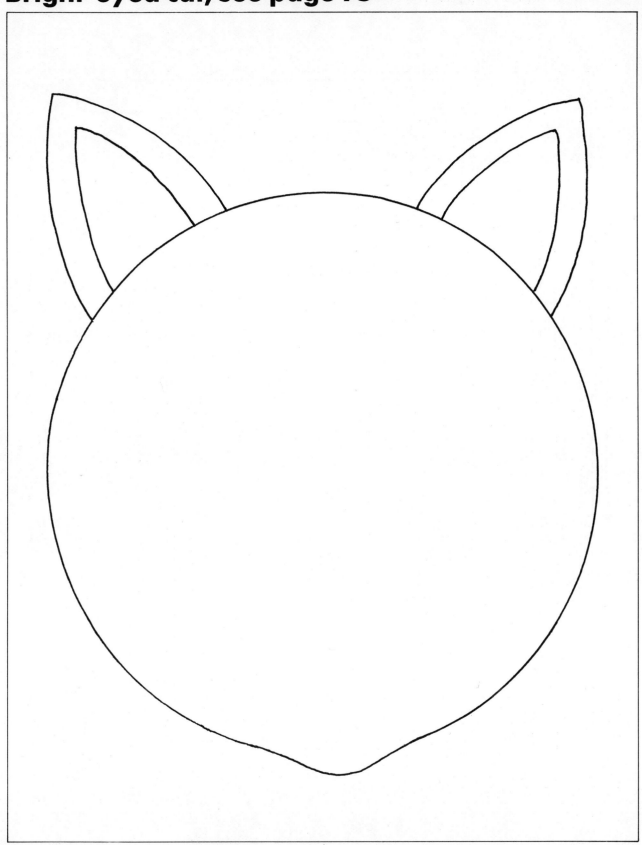

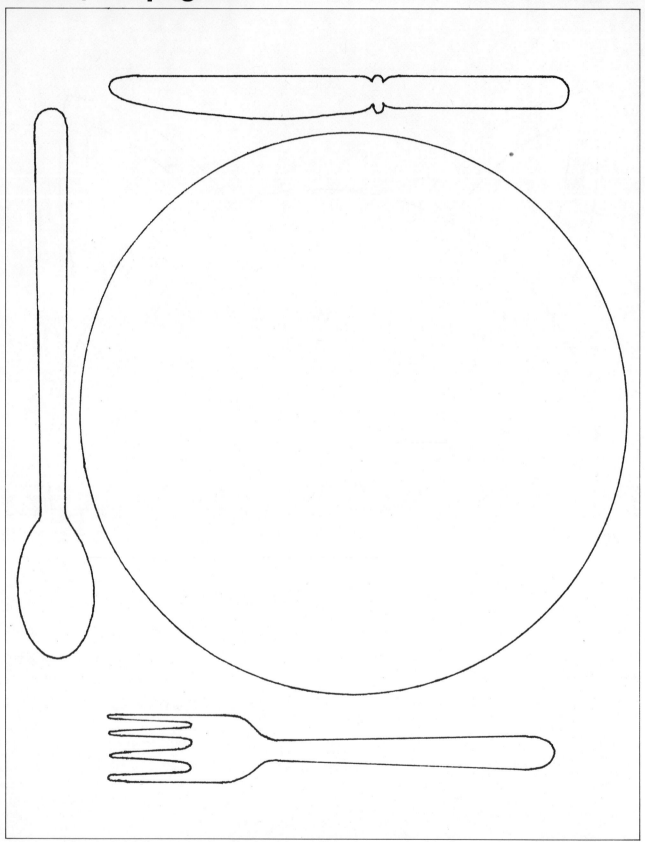